TRACTION ENGINES

TRACTION ENGINES

TWO CENTURIES OF STEAM

ANTHONY BURTON

CHARTWELL
BOOKS, INC.

Published by
CHARTWELL BOOKS, INC.
A Division of **BOOK SALES, INC.**
114 Northfield Avenue
Edison, New Jersey 08837

ISBN: 0-7858-1172-9

Editorial and design by
Amber Books Ltd
Bradley's Close
74–77 White Lion Street
London N1 9PF

Project Editor: Antonia Maxwell
Design: Zoë Mellors
Picture Research: Lisa Wren

Printed in Italy

FRONTISPIECE: A splendid Burrell showman's engine, its generator wired up for electrical supply.

CONTENTS PAGE: Showmen's engines on parade.

CONTENTS

CHAPTER 1

GETTING UP STEAM

For many it is a summer ritual that begins at a temporary car park in a field. The modern vehicle safely stowed away, the enthusiast sets off, following his nose as an irresistible aroma is carried across the hedgerows. That unique scent, made up of hot oil and coal, means just one thing – the steam fair. The engines themselves are traction engines, ploughing engines, showmen's engines, steam rollers, and perhaps the occasional steam wagon and steam car. They are giants from a past age, but one not so very far away that there are not some left who can remember them when they were more than just exhibits. However, even the best of the steam fairs cannot altogether capture the days when these great engines were not just there to be admired, but were part of the everyday working life of town and country. For more than a century they did their work, and then their day was over. This is a book about the working engines, what they did and what they meant to the world of work. But where did it all begin?

The idea of using steam as a source of power goes right back to the ancient Greeks, but for all practical purposes it began at

ABOVE: The beginning of the steam age: a Newcomen engine which dates back to about 1712, here photographed in the nineteenth century in Shropshire, England.

LEFT: This Burrell showman's engine is not just an ornate machine: it comes into its own at night, when it is set to work generating electricity to light the fairground rides.

the end of the seventeenth century in the dark, damp world of Britain's mines. The deeper the mines were sunk, the worse the problem of flooding became and the greater the need for a new, efficient pump. The first man to come up with a viable solution was a Dartmouth blacksmith, Thomas Newcomen (1663–1729). A good deal of his business came from supplying tools to the tin and copper mines of Devon and Cornwall, so he was well aware of the problem. A mine pump is a simple enough piece of equipment, requiring pump rods that can move up and down in the mine shaft. The down part is easy – gravity takes care of that. However, a device was needed that would raise the heavy rods up again. Newcomen hung his pump rods from one end of a massive overhead beam pivoted at its centre. The other end of the beam was attached by a chain to a piston set in an open topped cylinder. Steam was passed into the cylinder, then condensed by spraying it with cold water, creating a near vacuum. Now air pressure forced the piston down and as it dropped down the cylinder, the giant beam rocked and the pump rods rose. With the pressure equalised, the whole cycle could begin again.

As a pumping engine this was a great success, but it was horribly inefficient in terms of fuel. This was no problem in the coalfields where poor coal, broken lumps, indeed almost anything, could be fed into the firebox at virtually no cost to the owner. It mattered a great deal in the metal mines of the West Country however, where coal had to be brought in by sea and

taken across rough country roads by horse and cart. The first Newcomen engine was installed at Dudley in the Black Country in 1712, but half a century was to pass before a scientist at Glasgow University, baffled that his model Newcomen engine was not working properly, passed the problem to the University instrument maker, James Watt (1736–1819). He realised that the problem lay with constantly reheating the cylinder after cooling it with the water spray. His answer was to have a separate vessel into which the steam could be drawn and condensed. This was fine as far as it went, but the cylinder could not be kept hot if the top was left open to the air, and here the crucial change was made. Watt closed the cylinder, and used steam pressure instead of air pressure to move the piston.

THE AGE OF STEAM

Now this may sound all rather uninspiringly technical, but the implications were not just enormous, they would literally change the world. Because the cylinder was closed, steam could be alternately admitted above and below the piston. Newcomen's piston was only powered for the down stroke, but Watt's could be moved both up and down. With this reciprocal motion, it was a simple matter to add in a mechanical linkage, such as a crank, which would turn it into circular motion. Watt went into partnership with a Birmingham entrepreneur, Matthew Boulton, and together they acquired patents which, in effect, gave them a monopoly of steam engine development until the end of the eighteenth century. The Boulton and Watt engine soon took over from the Newcomen in Cornwall as an efficient pump, but it also found a new role as a device to work machinery, just as the water wheel had done for many centuries. For once you have a rotating shaft all you need is a simple system of belts and pulleys to run a whole series of different machines. The age of the steam factory had arrived and life would never be the same again.

If the steam engine can turn the wheels of a factory, why not mount it on wheels and let it drive itself along? Here a literally huge problem appeared. Watt was a fervent believer in using steam at low pressure, scarcely more than that of the atmosphere, and the machines were necessarily vast. For example, the oldest surviving Boulton and Watt engine, still able to do the work it was built to do, stands at Crofton by the Kennet and Avon Canal in southwest England, and it has been there since 1812. Like the Newcomen engine, this is a beam engine, standing in a three-storey engine house. It is a monster of a machine, with an overhead beam of 29ft (9m) and weighing 6 tons. At

LEFT: An Aveling and Porter roller, complete with its living van and water cart, gets an enthusiastic welcome from local schoolchildren, hoping for a ride.

ABOVE: In the eighteenth century, the steam engine was a massive machine, used mainly for pumping. Here a Boulton and Watt beam engine is exposed during demolition of its Birmingham engine house.

each nod of its head, the water gushes at the rate of over 100,000 gallons (450,000 litres) per hour. It is mightily impressive, but there is no way it could be mounted on wheels and driven around the countryside. When Boulton and Watt wanted more power they simply made bigger engines, and it was not unusual to have cylinders up to 6ft (2m) in diameter. The alternative was to use steam at higher pressure in smaller cylinders, but that was anathema to Watt. As he had taken out patents which gave him a virtual monopoly of steam engine development, there was no way that high-pressure engines could be developed in Britain until his patents ran out at the end of the eighteenth century. But the patent stopped at the English Channel, and over in continental Europe others were thinking about different ways of using steam.

EUROPEAN INNOVATIONS

The French physicist Denis Papin had worked as an assistant to the great Dutch scientist Christian Huygens (1629–95) and he set about devising a machine very like Newcomen's, producing a working model as early as 1690. He never got around to constructing an actual engine, but his scientific ideas were published and studied. Among those who took a keen interest was a former officer in the Austro-Hungarian army, Nicolas Joseph Cugnot. He served throughout the Seven Years War (1756–63) at the end of which he retired to Paris where he busied himself with inventions and research, including research into steam power. As an army officer he was well aware of the problems of using large teams of horses to haul heavy artillery around the battlefield, and began to think of using a steam-powered vehicle instead. The result was the world's first vehicle to be moved by anything other than animals or the natural forces of wind and water. It was, in fact, the first steam tractor. A prototype was built in 1769 and a second improved version appeared a year later. This is now preserved in the Conservatoire des Arts et Métiers in Paris. It is a curious, ungainly object on three wheels. It has two cylinders, one on each side of the single front wheel. Unlike the Boulton and Watt engines, the steam was not condensed, but produced at high pressure so that it expanded in the cylinders to move the pistons. The boiler was alarmingly set in a bracket right at the front, and steering was by a tiller arrangement to the driving wheel.

With hindsight, it is easy to see just how important the Cugnot machine really was. Here was a small, high-pressure steam engine working on a single driving wheel that could move a 4-ton load at a modest walking speed. There were, however, several problems that Cugnot never overcame. The first was that after twenty minutes the boiler ran dry and there would be

a further twenty minutes wait before steam could be raised again. A machine that had to have a twenty-minute rest after just one mile of travel was not greeted with great enthusiasm by the military authorities. More serious in some ways was its sheer uncontrollability. It wobbled alarmingly and the precariously hung boiler made it desperately unstable. According to some reports, which may well be apocryphal, after hitting a brick wall and overturning on a roadway, the authorities had Cugnot arrested before he could do any more damage. True or not, no more was heard of Cugnot and his military tractor and any chance of further advances in France were brought to an end by the French Revolution (1789). The story of the steam engine moved back to Britain, where the revolution was industrial rather than political.

RAISING THE PRESSURE

Boulton and Watt may have set their minds firmly against high-pressure steam, but that did not prevent their agent in Cornwall, William Murdoch, indulging in a little experimentation on his own account. Murdoch came from an inventive family. His father, John Murdoch, designed an early form of bicycle which was described as having been worked by a pair of handles oper-

BELOW: The very first application of steam power to move a vehicle down a road: Nicolas Joseph Cugnot's steam tractor of 1770, now preserved in Paris.

ating a ratchet on the driving wheel. Dr Johnson (1709–84), for one, was unimpressed: 'Then, Sir, what is gained is, the man has a choice whether he will move himself alone, or himself and the machine too' (*Life of Samuel Johnson*, James Boswell, 1791), showing that however witty and learned he might have been, he had a very poor knowledge of mechanics. Murdoch, however, set out to build a 'road locomotive', which was to be almost as ungainly as Cugnot's. It had a vertical cylinder set directly in the boiler, and the drive to the cranked axle was by a long, overhead beam, which must have given a very uneven motion. Because of the direct link to the axle, there could be no springing, and would have produced an interesting ride on the very rough roads of the day! Steering was by a single front wheel and, as there was no gearing, one of the wheels had to be allowed to run free of the axle.

Murdoch was very secretive, and he had every reason to be. His employers were notoriously opposed to any such experiments, and what was worse, he was surrounded by steam engineers who bitterly resented the Boulton and Watt monopoly. He would sneak out at night to test his tiny engine. The results were sometimes a little startling, as when he made a trial run near Camborne church.

The night was dark, and he alone sallied out with his engine, lighted the fire or lamp under the boiler, and started the locomotive with the Inventor in full chase after it. Shortly after he heard distant despair – like shouting, it was too dark to perceive objects, but he soon found that the cries for assistance proceeded from the worthy pastor, who, going into the town on business, was met in the lonely road by the fiery monster, who he subsequently declared he took to be the Evil One.
(from a paper presented to the *Institution of Mechanical Engineers* by a Mr Buckle, October 1850)

The 'fiery monster' never got beyond the model stage, and the original itself is now in the Birmingham City Museum.

Murdoch worked on his steam carriage on and off during the 1780s. The big question that has never been, and probably never will be, resolved is whether other engineers in Cornwall knew of its existence and the principles on which it worked – in particular, a near neighbour of Murdoch's who was already acquiring a reputation for his brilliance as an engineer and steam man, Richard Trevithick (1771–1833). There is some evidence to suggest that he did know of Murdoch's work, but

RIGHT: The first passenger-carrying steam carriage built in Britain by Richard Trevithick in 1801. This is a model for a full-scale replica built to celebrate its bi-centenary.

ABOVE: Tom Brogden's working replica of Trevithick's London carriage. The engineer stood on the platform at the back, while the steerer tried to cope with the awkward tiller.

Trevithick himself strenuously denied it. He certainly wouldn't have had access to it out of friendship, for Trevithick was among those who fought hardest against the Boulton and Watt monopoly and tried to build engines of his own, bringing him injunctions and law suits. However, it was to be Trevithick who would move the story of steam forward in the most decisive manner.

If Watt hated high-pressure steam, Trevithick loved it. He realised that with high-pressure steam, engines no longer needed to be fixed in great houses of stone, but could be taken to where they were needed. His first thoughts were centred on the idea of building portable engines, which became known as 'puffers', because instead of condensing the steam it was puffed out into the air. From here it was not a very big step to think of an engine that could move itself. He set to work designing his first engine in 1800, and a year later he had a full-sized machine ready for trial. It was, in effect, one of his 'puffers' set on wheels. There was a little platform at the front where Trevithick could feed the boiler, which had a return flue, turning through a U-bend so that fire grate and chimney were both at the same end. He could also manipulate the steam controls and steer the engine. At the rear was the water tank, and a second platform from which water levels could be tested, and the feed pump activated to keep the boiler topped up when necessary. The cylinder was set vertically in the boiler and drove the rear wheels via cross heads. Steering was via a pole attached to the pivoted front axle of the four-wheeled vehicle. Eventually all was ready and a local cooper, Stephen Williams, gave this account of the great day:

In the year 1801, upon Christmas-eve, coming on evening,
Captain Dick [Trevithick] got up steam, out on the high-road, just
opposite the shop at the Weith. When we heard that Captain Dick was
agoing to turn on steam, we jumped on as many as could:
may be seven or eight of us. 'Twas a stiffish hill going from the Weith up
to Camborne Beacon, but she went up like a little bird.
When she had gone about a quarter of a mile, there was a roguish piece
of road covered with loose stones; she didn't go quite so fast, and as it
was a flood of rain, and we were very squeezed together, I jumped off.
She was going faster than I could walk, and went on up
the hill about a quarter or half a mile farther, when they
turned her and came back again to the shop.
(Life of Richard Trebithick, Francis Trevithick, 1872)

It was a triumph; the locomotive had more than proved its worth. However, disaster soon followed. Other runs were made over the next few days and on one of these a problem that was to plague all early attempts to put steam on the road put in an appearance. The combination of poor, bumpy surfaces and a far from satisfactory steering system resulted in the engine over-turning in a ditch. Trevithick was not a man to be unduly worried by such minor mishaps, so the engine was hauled under cover while he and his friends popped over the road to the local inn. Unfortunately, no one had thought to dowse the fire, and as the drinks were lowered on one side of the road, the pressure rose on the other until with an almighty bang, engine and shed were distributed around the neighbourhood.

Undeterred, Trevithick set out for London with a new version of his steam carriage. This was a genuine passenger coach, with a stage-coach body set in a sprung frame. In an attempt to overcome the rough road and steering problems, the rear drive wheels were enormous, 10ft (3m) in diameter, and the single front wheel was again controlled by a tiller. It might seem odd that such a primitive device was used, but it has to be remembered that no one had ever had to steer a vehicle before. Up to then, all you needed to do was steer the horses, and the coach automatically followed. Almost the only form of transport that did need steering were boats, so the tiller was duly adapted from these. The engine did, however, have a new element of sophistication: gears.

Round and round London Trevithick went on demonstration runs, and he must have been certain that there would be huge interest in and enthusiasm for his invention. This was to be the first horseless carriage, and that had to be a good thing. Today we look back on the age of the stage coach as a time of romantic, pollution-free beauty. What we prefer not to think about is the effect the natural functions of thousands of horses had on city streets. The worst of the mess was cleared off main roads by crossing sweepers, young lads dodging with brush and shovel between the hooves and the wheels. In the smarter parts of town, noise was reduced by paving the roads with wooden blocks, but these soaked up urine and on hot days the stench of ammonia was all but unbearable. Surely the world would turn with enthusiasm to the wonderful new machine. The world did not. The world ignored it. Incredibly, not a single mention of the very first mechanical passenger coach appeared in any of the London papers. Steam on the road excited no interest whatsoever.

PIONEERS OF THE ROAD

Although Trevithick's road carriage experiments came to an end, he did find a new use for the locomotive. In 1804 he set it on the rails of the Penydarren tramway in South Wales and the railway age was born. It did not, however, mean that experiments in steam on the road had ceased – far from it. Inevitably, the experiments were concentrated in Britain which in the first two decades of the nineteenth century had over ninety per cent of the world's stock of steam engines at work in mills, mines and factories. Among the notable pioneers were Goldsworthy Gurney, Walter Hancock and Sir Charles Dance. One of Gurney's other inventions is still with us, a fluted cast iron stove to be found vainly trying to impart warmth in cavernous cathedrals. His early experiments with road vehicles used mechanical legs instead of wheels, but were quickly abandoned. His later efforts were a good deal more practical and his best effort was the 'steam drag'. Like Cugnot's pioneering engine, this was in effect a tractor to which a passenger coach, or indeed a goods wagon, could be attached. It had one obvious advantage for the travelling public – passengers were safely detached from the power unit and the boiler which, in popular imagination at least, was likely to explode at any moment. In fact, the chief problem faced by Gurney proved not to be too much steam but too little. He made extravagant claims for his drag, which he said had run from London to Bath at an average speed of 15mph (24km/h). It is unlikely that this ever happened.

Hancock, too, got off to a distinctly wobbly start, but he soon found answers to some of the problems that had bedevilled other engineers. His boiler, looking very like an old-fashioned central heating radiator, was a good deal more effective than Gurney's, and he developed a form of chain drive to the rear

ABOVE: Walter Hancock's elaborately decorated steam omnibus, which ran very successfully in 1832, taking businessmen from Paddington Station in London to the City.

axle, which proved much more reliable than the cranked axle of other models. His engine went into service in the 1830s as a 14-seater omnibus for the London and Paddington Steam Carriage Company, running between Paddington and the City. It was a great success, but as is so often the case in the history of technology, the greed of the entrepreneur brought it all to nothing. The company had promised further orders if the trials were a success. Instead, they passed the whole thing to their own engineer, who took the engine to pieces and set about making cheap, shoddy copies. To the astonishment of the dishonest penny-pinchers, they were an utter failure and the whole venture collapsed. It was not the only scheme of its kind to have a promising start, but never to reach the end it deserved.

Sir Charles Dance, a former army officer and a wholly honourable man, bought three of Gurney's drags and in 1831 established a regular service between Gloucester and Cheltenham. There were four runs a day and in four months, 3000 contented passengers had been carried. So why did it end? There are two possible explanations, and the truth may well be that both contributed to the final decision. Firstly, the local authorities did not like steam. It was nothing to do with frightening the horses,

concerns for public safety, or anything that worthy. It quite simply cost more money to maintain a road fit for steam engines than it did for one only used by horses. So they upped the tolls on the steam drags to a ruinously high level. The other factor was reliability. The service was maintained, but it was said that when one drag was bowling along the road, the other two were being worked over by feverish mechanics. Very soon all experiments stopped, and the first golden age of steam on the road had ended with the light sadly dimmed.

There were many reasons for the failure, not least the inability of the engineers to solve all the practical problems of the new machines. Research and trials cost money, and with toll charges for steam vehicles steadily mounting, investors became ever harder to find. However, Trevithick struggled on with his road carriages, fighting the bad roads, trying to overcome the steering difficulties and struggling to fit the working parts into a small, economic space. When he finally put his engine on rails, most of these problems disappeared. The track was hard, level and smooth; steering was not needed at all and it was no longer necessary to pack all the working parts into a very tiny space. By 1831, the first inter-city rail line between Liverpool and

Manchester was opened for passengers and goods. The principal problems of engine building had been solved by Robert Stephenson with his famous locomotive *Rocket*. Railway mania swept the country and the network began to spread. Why bother with steam on the roads when steam on rails was so obviously superior? It was a view that the railway companies were eager to promote. They had invested a huge amount of money in track laying, and had absolutely no interest in seeing passengers or freight going to a rival steam service on the roads.

There was a real clash of interest here. Men who had spent their lives promoting canals and road improvements heartily detested the interloping railways. Thomas Telford (1757–1834), the Scottish civil engineer, was one of those who opposed them to the last, but he was an enthusiastic supporter of Dance and his steam service. In his view the future lay in moving heavy goods by canal and river and passengers by steam coaches on the ordinary roads. But that great steam man Isambard Kingdom Brunel (1806–59), builder of the mighty Great Western Railway, lost all his enthusiasm for steam as soon as he began to consider road traffic. He was not a great one for writing books and articles, life

was too busy for that, but he did take time off to contribute to a book *The Horse* by William Youatt (Chapman and Hall, 1843). In it he argued that there was simply no future in steam carriages and steam drags, claiming that 'beasts of draught, and particularly the horse, although the most ancient, still remain the most advantageous source of power'. And that, for many people, was that – the story was over. But it was not quite over, and it is time for one more look at Trevithick and his work. In 1812 the following advert appeared in the *Royal Cornwall Gazette*.

THRASHING MACHINE
To be sold by Private Contract,
a Two-Horse THRASHING MACHINE, allowed by mechanics to be the
best in the country. Apply to me; (my reason for selling the Horse
Machine is that I am about to have a Steam Engine to grind for the
poor, and the same power will work the Thrashing Mill;)
the Mill is adapted to grind 150 bushels corn per day.
RICHARD TREVITHICK
Engineer

If there was, as it seemed, to be no future for steam on the road, perhaps there was more hope down on the farm.

BELOW: Threshing in the 1890s. The man on the ladder is feeding hay into the threshing box, with both an Ivel tractor and a traction engine to provide the power.

CHAPTER 2

IN THE FIELDS

Huge improvements in agriculture had been made in Britain since Tudor times. These were largely made possible by the phasing out of the old open-field system, and its replacement by enclosures, fields neatly divided by fence and hedge. Now the farmer and landowner could set about the serious work of improving the land and its yields. New machines, such as Jethro Tull's famous seed drill invented in 1701, helped to reduce the hard labour of farming – and the farmer's wage bill. But of all the back-breaking jobs that fell to the farm labourer, few were worse than threshing, separating the grain from the straw and chaff. In Britain, this was winter work, where the grain was piled into barns and beaten with flails for hour after hour. It takes little imagination to conceive of the sheer tedium of endlessly flailing away with aching muscles, while the clouds of choking dust rise all around. In southern Europe, where the climate allowed a different approach, threshing could be maintained as an outdoor

activity, which was at least a good deal healthier. Circular floors made up of stone setts were built among the fields. The corn was laid on top, after which a man drove a weighted sledge, its bottom reinforced with metal plates, and hauled by mule or donkey, round and round on top of it. In some regions, the practice persists right through to the present day; the author picnicked by just such a threshing floor in the Spanish Sierras as recently as 1998.

In Britain, however, agricultural improvement was pursued with the greatest enthusiasm. As the Industrial Revolution gathered pace, so a movement began from country to town, and there was an urgent need for the countryside to produce more and more food with less and less human labour. Threshing was an obvious choice for mechanisation. All kinds of machines were tried. In 1732, for example, Michael Menzies, a Scottish advocate and inventor, built a machine powered by a water wheel turning a shaft with a number of flails fastened round it. Like the flail in the hand of the labourer, these mechanical scourges thumped away steadily at the grain laid on the floor. It was not a great success.

It was not until 1786 that a Scotsman, Andrew Meikle, designed and built a machine that was to be the model for all later development. Its great advantage was its simplicity. A drum was made to rotate at high speed inside a concave plate, with just

ABOVE: The huge steam engines of the eighteenth century gave way to compact portables like this German machine of 1888. With a set of wheels added, the traction engine was born.

LEFT: A scene that was to become increasingly common in the latter part of the nineteenth century – the specialist steam ploughing team hard at work.

a small gap between the two. Corn was fed in at the top and the grain removed by the rubbing action. The threshing drum became very popular, but it was not cheap. A power source was needed, and that was usually provided by horses walking round a circular track turning a shaft, attached through gearing to the drum. Arthur Young, who travelled throughout England in the early years of the nineteenth century reporting on agricultural matters, always made a note of the machines, and his reports tell us a great deal about how they worked and just as importantly who used them and what they would have cost. In Oxfordshire,

LEFT: A Ruston portable engine at work. It is easily distinguished from a traction engine by the shafts visible at the front, where the horse was harnessed.

BELOW: Germany's oldest agricultural engine. It was built by Wolf at Magdeburg-Buckau in the 1860s, and it remained in use for about half a century.

for example, he noted nine threshing mills and the owners included Lord Macclesfield, Lord Harcourt and the Bishop of Durham. Lord Macclesfield's mill was worked by four horses, the machinery cost £120 to make and erect and on top of that was the cost of the mill building itself. This was not something that could be slipped into the meagre budget of the average farmer, who could employ three men for a year for what it cost to build one threshing drum. However, there was no question that a new, efficient machine had been developed.

In America, the development of threshing machines followed a somewhat different route. The first real success was the result of a long period of development that was largely down to one man and the company which he was later to form. Jerome Increase Case left New York in 1842 and headed west to Wisconsin with his rather crude 'ground hog' thresher. If there was a need for an efficient machine in Britain, the need was far greater in the very thinly populated farmland of the Midwest. It was sufficiently

successful for him to establish a factory at Racine, on the shores of Lake Michigan. Case was not just a manufacturer, he was a passionate enthusiast, quite prepared to demonstrate the virtues of his machines in person. At one demonstration, he recorded that it had taken him just half a day to set up his rig and had gone on to thrash 177 bushels in the afternoon. Since he had written to his wife that 'all united in saying that if the machine could thrash 200 bushels in a day, it could not be equalled by any in the country' this was a more than a satisfactory result. His reputation as a hands-on manufacturer, who cared for his machines and was jealous of his reputation, was enhanced in a famous incident when a farmer complained that his new Case was not working as it should. Case went down in person, and when he could not make it work either, set fire to it and sent the farmer a new one. In 1862, he improved the drive to the thresher by introducing the Mounted Woodberry, in effect a more efficient form of horse whim (horse-drawn winch), where the driver controlled the circling horses from a central platform. Perhaps the most surprising

feature of the Case story is that he remained faithful to horses for so long. Case was to become world famous as a manufacturer of steam engines, yet the first one was not destined to appear until 1869.

A PORTABLE ENGINE

It was very clear that a machine that could be worked by horses moving round a circle could also be worked by a steam engine. It had already happened in the world of mining, where the horse whim used for hauling material up and down the shaft was being replaced by the steam whim. In fact, any form of agricultural processing of that kind could be turned over to steam. Back in Britain, Trevithick was one of the few engineers who not only worked at establishing steam on the farm, but who, when he set up a mill for Sir Christopher Hawkins of Trewithen in Cornwall, southwest England, in 1812 brought in three independent observers to observe the trials. Their report was admirably precise and splendidly encouraging:

... from the time the mill began to work, to two minutes after two o'clock, being four hours and three-quarters, 1500 sheaves of barley were thrashed clean, and one bushel of coal more was consumed. We think there was sufficient steam remaining in the boiler to have thrashed from 50 to 100 sheaves more barley, and the water in the boiler was by no means exhausted. We had the satisfaction to observe that a common labourer regulated the thrashing mill, and in a moment of time made it go faster, slower, or entirely to cease working. We approve of the steadiness and velocity with which the machine worked; and in every respect we prefer the power of steam, as here applied, to that of horses.

What was valuable for large farms in Britain was even more so for the larger plantations across the Atlantic. By 1812, Trevithick was supplying engines to work the sugar mills of the West Indies. An even more lucrative development appeared in the southern states of America where, in the 1790s, Eli Whitney invented a gin to strip the seeds out of the boll of the cotton plant. Here was another machine that could easily be worked by steam. Well-known manufacturers, such as Boulton and Watt, were soon sending engines to the plantations, and the Americans began to manufacture steam engines for themselves. Benjamin Latrobe, a Louisiana planter, was offering 12-hp engines for powering sugar mills at $2,500 each. The market was big and getting bigger: a survey of Louisiana in 1838 showed that one state alone had 274 stationary engines in use. This was all very fine for the big man with spare capital, but was still no help to the small farmer. Trevithick, who in these early days cannot be kept out of the story for long, was the first to realise that the answer lay with the portable, high-pressure steam engine that could be moved from farm to farm. He offered such engines for sale at the price of £65, and although that was still too much for the little man, it was possible for a number of farmers to get together and take it in turns to use the machine. Another alternative that was to become very popular in the years to come, was for a contractor to buy an engine and take it round the various farms, charging a fixed rate for his services. None of this happened with any great frequency, but the way forward for steam on the farm was being mapped out.

Development languished, but there were attempts to revive the flagging fortunes of the portable engine. There were real advances in design, and some of the names that were to become famous in the story of traction engine development began to appear. Robert Ransome was one of those extraordinary men who rose to eminence in the Industrial Revolution entirely through his own wits, ingenuity and hard work. Born in 1753, he began his working life as an apprentice to a Norwich ironmonger in southeast England. But selling was less interesting than manufacturing and in no time it seemed he had his own foundry and was turning out a brand new line in improved ploughshares. Success followed success and the firm moved to larger premises in Ipswich, where they were responsible for the ironwork for the town's new gas works. At the time of Ransome's death in 1830, the company was well and truly established and the new generation turned to steam.

One problem that had beset all the early developers was the innate conservatism of the farming community, reinforced by their isolation. It was rare for country people to travel far from home, but the spread of railways was slowly beginning to make a difference. There was an awareness, however, that new ideas and new technologies would not spread unaided. There were individual propagandists such as John Lathbury, who gave a talk

ABOVE: Thomas Aveling's traction engine of 1862. His first idea for steering, without the use of a horse, was to have a fifth wheel at the front, controlled by the steerer using a tiller.

on the advantages of steam threshing, which was fully written up in the *Farmer's Magazine* in 1844, so that it was received far outside his home territory. He spoke at length of the huge economies that were to be made, not least because the work was so much less demanding that the farmer was not required to spend a great deal of money on beer to keep the workers going! (It is not recorded how the audience received this news of reduced beer sales, for the talk was given in Burton-on-Trent, the most famous centre for brewing in the whole country.) There were royal societies for the propagation of arts and sciences, but until 1839 none was specifically directed to encouraging and spreading new ideas in farming. That year, however, The Royal Agricultural Society was founded and one of their first acts was to establish annual royal shows, and to make sure that the word was widely spread, they were held at different sites each year. The shows were an immense success, so much so that in 1841 Ransomes were prepared to make the long journey by horse and cart all the way from Ipswich to London to show off their new portable engine. This was more than just another portable engine, it was one with a crucial difference. It had no need for a team of horses to drag it from farm to farm – it drove

itself. A sprocket drive now ran from the engine shaft to one of the rear wheels: the portable engine had become a traction engine. It was not quite free of traditional horse power, however. Ransomes were faced with the problem that had beset the steam carriage developers before them – how to steer the brute. Their answer was to put shafts on the front and harness up a horse as a four-legged steerer.

If Ransomes had been content with just one innovation then they might have had a winner, but they set to work on lengthening the chassis so that the threshing drum could be incorporated into one composite machine. The Royal Agricultural Society was delighted and gave it the top award of the year. For the farmers it was one innovation too many. They might have been prepared to get rid of their old portable for a better model, but to get rid of engine and thresher was too much. There was little or no interest in the hybrid, and Ransomes were forced to drop the whole idea, though they were by no means finished in the business. By 1849, they were at the Leeds Royal Show, with the 'Farmer's Engine', this time without the horse as they had introduced steering to the front wheels, and the threshing engine was no longer an integral part.

The design was good, but proved too light for the heavy work of threshing.

It was not the only farmer's engine to be offered at this time. In America and Canada, the great westward movement was under way and with it came the vast acres of cereal farms. In countries where labour was scarce and animal power was expensive, the appeal of the portable steam engine was obvious and American manufacturers were not slow to see the opportunity. A.L. Archambault of Philadelphia offered engines in three sizes, 4hp, 10hp and 20hp, although they appear to have been a little fragile – the horizontal boiler was mounted on a chassis carried on four tiny wooden wheels. Rather more ambitiously, Charles Hoad and Gilbert Bradford took their design to the New York State Fair of 1851 where, like their British counterpart the Ransomes, they won an award, but failed to get the orders. However, at least the subject was now being given serious consideration, and no doubt there would have been the sort of steady progress that was soon to be found in Britain, if the country had not slid into the disaster of the Civil War (1861–5).

PIONEERS: AVELING AND GARRETT

All the early advances had been made by engineers who had taken an interest in farming. One of the next big steps forward was to be made by a British farmer who discovered he had a taste and flair for engineering. Thomas Aveling was born in Cambridgeshire in 1824 and brought up under the harsh discipline of a strict stepfather. His schooling was brief, and he was shot off as soon as possible as an apprentice to a local farmer. The mysteries of animal husbandry and crops were far less interesting to him than the intricacies of farm machinery. He began by repairing implements on his employer's farm, and soon found himself in demand. From there it was just one more step to the realisation that not only could he repair the unreliable machines of the time, but he could devise improvements as well. The transition was gradual from repair man to manufacturer, but by 1850 he had his own works at Rochester.

A man of his ability was bound, sooner or later, to turn his attention to the most exciting development of the day, the portable engine, and what he saw annoyed him. 'It is an insult to mechanical science, to see half a dozen horses drag along a steam engine, and the sight of six sailing vessels towing a steamer would certainly not be more ridiculous' (*A Hundred Years of Road Rollers*, Aveling & Barford, 1965). Of course, he was right; it was absurd at a time when locomotives were steaming at speed all over the brand new railway system that was spreading not just across Britain but throughout the world. He had a portable made by the Lincoln firm of Clayton and Shuttleworth and set about adapting it. He added a driving chain to link the crankshaft to the rear axle and away it puffed. But, of course, having been designed for hauling by a team of horses, the portable had no steering mechanism, and Aveling was forced to adopt the method first used by Ransomes. At least he was able to get rid of most of the 'ridiculous' horses, retaining just one for steering. Happy with the result, he took out a patent, but had to find money and resources before it could go into serious manufacture. What could be more natural than to look to the firm whose portable had been adapted in the first place, Clayton and Shuttleworth. They showed commendable enthusiasm, and Aveling was now able to work on an original design, rather than an adaptation. The first casualty was the horse, though the solution looks as incongruous to us as the team of draught horses did to Aveling. The shafts were retained, but between them instead of the horse was a single wheel mounted on a bracket. A long pole extended from the top of the bracket to a steerer who perched precariously just in front of the boiler, using the pole as an unwieldy tiller. This had all the disadvantages of early carriage steering, and must have made control on bumpy roads difficult, while the hapless steerer seemed in real danger of being jolted off right in front of the massive engine wheels.

Aveling was not alone in using chain drive. Richard Garrett and Sons of Leiston, Suffolk, also hit on the idea. Richard Garrett was in a very different position from Aveling. He was the third generation in the business. His grandfather had begun with a forge in the Suffolk town in the 1780s. Richard Garrett II had married the daughter of John Balls who, in 1805, had invented one of the most successful of all threshing machines, variously known as the 'drum' or the 'box'. The following year it was being manufactured by Garrett, and threshers were to be an important part of the firm's output for a hundred years. It was the third Richard Garrett who brought a whole new spirit and enterprise to the business when he took over in 1826. By 1830 he was employing sixty men, making everything from cooking stoves to seed drills. He moved into portable steam engines in 1847, and by 1851 the firm was big enough to be invited to show their wares at the Great Exhibition. Garrett was a man of vision and the experience of going to the Crystal Palace exhibition had its effect. In particular, he saw the advances being made in America, not just in agricultural machines, such as the famous McCormick reaper, but also in manufacturing processes. Robbins and Lawrence of Windsor, Vermont, for example, were producing rifles with interchangeable parts and these were widely admired. It was clear to Garrett that there was something going on across the water that he ought to know about, and he set off for America. What he discovered was the process of mass production, albeit still in its infancy. He came back in 1852 and at once ordered work to start on his 'Long Shop'.

This extraordinary building was known locally as 'the cathedral' and, with its tall, wooden columns dividing the long, high

ABOVE: A Sawyer and Massey engine at work at a steam fair at Milton, Ontario. The machinery is driven by the continuous belt which is wrapped round the powerful-looking flywheel.

building into something like a nave and side aisles, it is not hard to see why. It was here that Garrett's machines were to be built. The individual parts were manufactured in the side aisles, while the machine was trundled down the centre, parts being steadily added as it went. In 1863, work began on the 'self-moving portable'. By now, however, it was becoming clear to engineers that simply devising methods to move standard portables around was only one step along the path they should be following. It was time, in fact, to think of the problem as a whole; time to design a machine in which the movement of the engine over the ground was at least as important as its ability to turn machinery. It was time, in short, to build a genuine traction engine

There were now more manufacturers in the field, some such as John Fowler of Leeds and Charles Burrell of Thetford, whose names live on in the world of preserved engines, and there were others, such as William Bray of Folkestone, who are today large-ly forgotten. Looking now at the engines of the mid-nineteenth

century, it should be remembered that designers could not advance any further than the technology of the time would allow. There was nothing wrong with chain drive in principle, indeed the fault lay with the chains themselves. Chain-making was closer to the craft of the blacksmith than it was to an effi-cient industrial process, and they were, quite literally, the weak link. As there was no sign of improvement in chain manufacture, which was mostly carried out in small workshops in the West Midlands, the designers were forced to seek alternatives. The obvious solution was to transfer the drive from the crankshaft to the rear wheels through gears. It is here that William Bray appears in the story, producing an all-gear drive as early as 1856. His engines also had a different steering mechanism from Aveling's. The front wheels were mounted in front of the boiler, and the steerer stood over them with a spoked wheel and a chain connection to a drum mounted above the axle. The device was obviously adapted from ocean vessels, where a ship's wheel was connected by chains to the rudder. A more elegant version was soon designed, the chain and bobbin, which could be operated from the footplate or manstand so that steerer and driver stood side by side, which if it did nothing else at least made communication a good deal easier.

By now the traction engine was nearing its familiar form. A multi-tubed boiler was used, a development which had first appeared on the railways in Robert Stephenson's locomotive Rocket in 1829. The steam-jacketed cylinder was set just above the firebox, with the crankshaft, bearing a large flywheel to ensure regular motion, set just in front of the chimney. This allowed for a shorter chain drive to be used. The water tank and fuel bunker were both integrated into the frame. The early engines were unsprung, and springing was considered something of a luxury in an engine that was destined to spend most of its working life standing still in a field, and even when it did move only travelling short distances at a modest walking pace. It is very doubtful if customers even considered the need for springs, but engineers do like solving problems – and springing was a difficult one. It was easy to apply springing to the front axle, but springing the drive axle without upsetting the movement of gears was a different matter. Various solutions were offered. Fowler made sprung wheels, or more accurately sprung spokes that could absorb the shock, while Burrell went for a sprung drive axle, the movement compensated for by a very

elaborate system involving a countershaft. The real demand for springing, however, only appeared with the development of road haulage.

As early as the late eighteenth century, engineers had realised that if you used high-pressure steam, then the exhaust steam would still be under pressure when it was blown away in the wind. The answer was to build a second cylinder alongside the first, but of greater diameter to allow for the reduced pressure while still retaining the system in balance. This was the compound steam engine. Garrett demonstrated their first compound in 1879, and both Fowler and Aveling were building very successful compound traction engines by the 1880s.

WORLD DEVELOPMENTS

Not all traction engine manufacturers followed British ideas. In Europe, the French and Germans often favoured vertical boilers. In British engines, the boiler was a major element in providing the rigid frame, but in the European models there was a separate chassis. It was quite common to use three-wheelers, an arrangement almost unheard of in Britain. In America, manufacturers, such as Avery, favoured undermounted engines, that is

BELOW: The other end of the operation shown opposite. The belt can be seen working the thresher, which is being fed with hay from the cart by an operator or 'feeder'.

with the cylinders and pistons below the boiler. There was one other major change which, although it had its origins in Britain, was to be developed in America. As early as 1825, Sir George Cayley had devised what we now call the caterpillar track. A flexible band of joined metal plates ran round the two driving wheels, while smaller wheels in between provided support – exactly what we see today in an army tank. Bizarrely, however, British engineers were unimpressed and preferred an alternative system devised by John Boydell. He called it a track layer, and it consisted of four or five metal plates fastened on the outside of the drive wheels. As the wheels turned, the plates flopped down, providing a continuous flat track for the vehicle. The problem lay not so much with the idea as with the practice – small stones clogged the movement, large ones smashed the plates. The Americans, very sensibly, went with the caterpillar track. Thomas S. Minnis of Pennsylvania took out a patent in 1867 and by 1869 his 'crawler' was at work. No one could call it an elegant machine, with its vertical boiler stuck up on an ungainly frame and its three sets of tracks, one at the front and two at the rear. The system was widely adopted by two companies, Holt and Best, who after years of bitter rivalry joined forces to create a new enterprise that was to become the world-famous Caterpillar Company.

The contrast between British and American builders could hardly have been greater. Where the former tended to move ever closer together in terms of design, the Americans seemed to delight in variety – overmounted, undermounted, vertical boilers, horizontal boilers, three wheels, four wheels, engines that were the giants of the steam world. And they needed to work hard. The great wheat fields of North America offered a very different challenge from the tiny hedged enclosures of England. It is doubtful if the English farmer could even imagine the scale of something like the Glenn Ranch of California, where the wheat field stretched away for a full 16 miles (26km) without a hedge or fence in sight. It was here in 1879 that a Gaar Scott engine set a new record. Working from sunrise to sunset, one machine driving a Gaar Scott thresher dealt with 216m^3 (6183 bushels) of wheat. And that is a lot of wheat.

A HARD LIFE

Design is only a part of the story of the traction engine, a small part in some ways, for once designed and built the engines could look forward to years, even decades, of useful life. And much of that work would be in the hands of a threshing contractor. It was not an easy life. The first task was to get the engine

LEFT: This picture clearly shows the steering mechanism that replaced the fifth wheel of early traction engines. Chains from below the driving position turn the drum on the front axle.

and the train of machinery ready – the threshing drum itself, a trusser for making the straw into bales, an elevator for lifting them and sometimes a chaff cutter as well, which hacked the straw up for low-quality feed. Travel to the farm was not a speedy matter. The traction engine was never devised for fast running and in Britain was further hampered by Parliamentary legislation, such as the famous Red Flag Act, which decreed that all engines had to be preceded by a man walking 60 yards in front carrying a red flag as warning that a dangerous, hissing beast was on the loose along the highway. The idea was to allow those with horses to get them under control or remove them to safety. As horses were by then widely used in railway goods yards right alongside far larger locomotives, as well as in use on the farm during threshing and had, in the early days, even been used to steer the mechanical beasts, the legislation seemed nothing other than conservative prejudice against steam and the modern world. There will be more on what restrictive legislation and poor roads did to hamper movement in the next chapter, but one interesting feature of traction engine design also created its very own problem. In the early years, differential gears were unknown. If you turn a big engine round a sharp corner, then the outer wheel will be forced to travel a great deal further than the inner, and ideally the two wheels should be able to move at different speeds – hence the need for differential gears. The only answer for the traction engine was to remove the driving pin from one wheel so that it could freewheel and replace it once the corner had been negotiated.

Once the farm was reached – and a good deal of manoeuvring was needed to get into a field or a yard – the drum was pulled up in front of the first stack to be threshed. It would usually have to be levelled up with jacks and chocks, after which the engine would be run round the drum and lined up at just the right distance so that the belt fitted between the pulley on the drum and the flywheel on the engine was at just the right tension. This was a matter that called for a good eye and fine judgement on the part of the driver. Once everything was in place, all belts set up and the elevator in position, gears oiled and running smoothly, the actual work could begin. The thatch that had kept the stack dry was removed and the first sheath thrown to the cutter who sliced away the binding twine and passed it to the feeder, who spread it out carefully and began feeding it down the concave. Threshing had begun.

It was not too bad at first, but as the day progressed the clouds of dust grew ever denser and more choking. It was not very hard work tossing sheaves down from the top of the stack, but as the stack shrunk a point was reached where the pitcher was having to throw them up to the cutter. It was not work for the squeamish either. The rats and mice who thought that they had found a nice warm home, complete with built-in larder, burrowed down as the stack diminished until there was nowhere else to go, and then they bolted – a trouser leg was considered by them to be a particularly good bolt hole, and twine was fastened around the trouser legs of the men just below the knee to prevent unwelcome visitors.

LIFE ON THE FARM

The pattern of life for the men depended very much on how far from home they were working. They were prepared for an hour or more's walk at each end of the working day for the pleasure of sleeping in their own beds, but this was not always possible. There were lodgings, but not many landladies looked kindly on men covered in soot, oil and straw. By the 1880s, the 'living van' had been added to the train. It was not exactly a model of comfort, offering no more than the basic amenities of bunk, stove and store cupboard, though a van produced by the engine-makers, Fowler, also had a desk so that the driver-foreman could keep up with the paperwork – if nothing else this shows that traction engine men were not the illiterates they were sometimes portrayed to be. The pub was an attractive draw at the end of a day spent breathing in dust, but there was not much time for indulgence, for the working day was long.

It took a good hour to clean out the firebox and tubes, light the fire and raise steam for a start that was seldom later than 7 a.m.. Work went on through the day, usually with a short stop for breakfast and perhaps half an hour for lunch. Threshing generally stopped around 5 p.m., but work was not over for the engine man who had to remove clinker and ashes, tend to the lubrication and generally check that all was well before the engine was sheeted over and put away for the night. The nearest most of us get today to any understanding of the thresher is when we see demonstrations at fairs. It is a delight to see the drum, visibly rocking on its wheels, hear the regular thump of the hard-working engine and enjoy the sight of the ancillary machines at work. Balers are always an attraction, as the metal arm pivots and nods like a giraffe at feeding time. What we do not get is any sense of the sheer hard work of the men who worked 12 hours a day and more, often in the most atrocious conditions. However, although it may all seem desperately hard to us, it was not especially harsh by the standards of the time, and was comparable to the life of the ploughman, who had to devote at least as much time to his horses at each end of the working day as the engine man did with his machine. Both were seen as being among the elite of agricultural workers and were rewarded accordingly, though they remained poor enough for all that. Both had skills which others knew nothing of, and took an intense pride in their work and in their charges. The ploughman would neatly plait the horses' tails and braid them, and even hang bells on the harness – four for each of the two lead horses, three each for the other pair and all 'tuned harmoniously' as one put it (quoted in *Labouring Life in the Victorian Countryside*, Pamela Horn, 1976). The engine man kept his brasses polished and his paintwork gleaming, and would look after even quite major repairs himself. He was quite capable, for example, of replacing a damaged boiler tube. To the ploughman, his horses

were all important – one recalled how he used to steal linseed cake, intended for the sheep, just to get a glossier coat on his horses. It all came down to the same thing, whether horse power or steam power, pride in the job.

North America had quite different problems. British engine men would have looked with envy at the later generation of traction engines, such as the Russell, with its enclosed cabin but neat sliding windows, very like those of a railway carriage, yet they never had to experience the bitter winds that blow across the North American prairies all the way from the Arctic Circle. With

BELOW: Although Britain led the way in the development of agricultural engines, they did not have a monopoly. This 1924 German Heucke enjoys the luxury of a covered cab.

vast areas to be covered and a much more thinly spread population, labour was always a problem here. The answer to stacking straw was found in a pneumatic conveyor known as the 'wind stacker' that carried the straw away from the drum. A cunning group of businessmen got together in 1891 and managed to acquire all the patents for the pneumatic conveyor system, after which they formed themselves into the Indiana Manufacturing Company. In fact they had no need to manufacture anything at all, nor did they – all they had to do was to collect $30 on every stacker sold no matter who had made it. Each one that went out bore a little plaque announcing another sale of 'The Farmer's Friend Stacker' and within ten years of acquiring the patents they had collected in over a quarter of a million dollars.

The British farmer, however, came at the end of a long tradition. His corn might well be sent for grinding to a watermill, mentioned in sources as early as the Domesday Book of 1086. He looked on permanence and continuity as the ultimate virtues. The farmers who made their way west were undertaking a great adventure, where precedents did not exist and where there was a whole new world to explore. Change was the watchword, not continuity; new was always better than old. Manufacturers realised that different countries called for different engines. If roads were bad in Britain and Europe they were often worse or non-existent in the newly opened-up territories. Some might want reassuring solidity and strength – others might have lower standards, sometimes a good deal lower. Few were as candid as the Port Huron Company of America, who specialised in threshing engines with straw-burning fireboxes. Their catalogue from the end of the nineteenth century set out just what was on offer from different manufacturers.

There are three classes of traction engines.
Heavy Weight, as English makes. - Built much heavier in
some parts than necessary for the work they have to do.
Middle Weight. - Port Huron, correctly proportioned.
Each part designed especially for the work it has
to do and the strain it has to stand.
Light Weight. - Those American and Canadian makes
built with the sole idea of making them of light
weight without regard to
correct proportions.
(Steam Carriages, William Fletcher, 1904)

LEFT: The great power of the agricultural steam engine is depicted by this Fowler ploughing engine, with its two cylinders set just behind the chimney.

Perhaps wisely, they did not name the manufacturers in the third class. The American engines were also different in other ways. They tended to run faster than their English equivalents and many followed the Port Huron example of providing fireboxes that could burn straw, with the extra essential of having bulbous spark-arresting chimneys.

The traction engine remained closely associated with threshing but could, of course, be put to other uses around the farm and on the land. It was a splendid workhorse that proved its worth in over a century of use, but it could not do everything. In particular it could not be used directly for ploughing – the great weight on the wheels produced ruts that were wholly unacceptable and undid any good work that the plough share

LEFT: The working lives of traction engines may well be over, but they can still be seen, proudly lined up for inspection, at steam fairs around the world.
BELOW: Fowell of St Ives, England, were one of the smaller manufacturers, working from 1878 to 1922. This 1910 engine seems to have the whole family on board.

might be doing. Engineers had to look for new solutions if steam was to play a role in digging and ploughing the land. Ploughing itself was a slow, laborious process and old practices lived on for a surprisingly long time – ploughing with oxen survived in Britain long enough to be photographed. Old designs, such as the Norfolk wheel plough and the wooden Essex swing plough, were still to be found at work as late as the 1930s. The nineteenth-century engineers who looked at the plough teams of heavy horses were not greatly impressed by their efficiency: they were able to turn little more than 1 acre (0.4ha) a day. So they began by looking at alternative ways of digging over the ground that might be more easily adapted for steam power.

APPLICATION AND INVENTION

We have not heard of Richard Trevithick for a little time, but he enters the story again as one of the pioneers. He was convinced that there was nothing on the farm powered by beast or man that could not be improved by the application of steam. He built the 'tormentor' – not a bad name for a device that ripped the ground apart. It was relatively crude, consisting of a carriage

bearing a circular frame rotated by gearing from the rear axle. Sharp, spade-like blades mounted round the rim cut up the earth as the contraption was hauled along by cable, wound in by a steam engine. It first appeared in 1813 and disappeared almost at once. A not dissimilar device was tried in France by Pierre Barrat in 1847, based on the mattock (a type of large pick) instead of the spade, but its main problem lay in overelaboration, as the mattocks were given both a digging and a twisting motion. Its fate was that of Trevithick's, in that it ultimately failed and was forgotten. Unusually in the story of steam on the farm, the middle of the nineteenth century seemed to be a time when Britain was not at the forefront of development, in spite of a tempting £500 prize offered by the Royal Agricultural Society to the successful inventor of a steam cultivator. It may have been the severity of the conditions laid down for the competition that actually hindered development. In trying to meet them all, inventors almost invariably failed, whereas a step-by-step approach could well have produced better results. The conditions were first that the successful machine had to work as well as a spade in turning the ground. This in itself acted as a disincentive to concentration on ploughing. The machine had to work any soil at various depths and cause no more damage to the land than the hooves of a horse team. It had to deal with weeds, invert grass, be easy to use and cost no more than the equivalent horses and implements. It was not merely a tall order but, in terms of available technology, all but impossible. As British inventors struggled, news was coming in of successes elsewhere in the world.

One of the most promising developments came from a Canadian, Robert Romaine. He would not have won the Royal Agricultural Society prize, for his machine was not self-propelling. He was happy to let horses do the pulling, while he concentrated on designing an efficient rotary cultivator. His machine had the added advantage of versatility. Realising that a machine that could only be used for part of the year was not as attractive as one with a wide variety of uses, he arranged the mechanism so that the rotor blades could be replaced by cutter blades turning it into a mechanical reaper. This required a further adaptation so that it could be pushed instead of pulled to avoid the horses' hooves damaging the crop. It was certainly a good idea, but the production model sadly failed to live up to expectations. He did, however, eventually go on to produce a more successful self-propelled cultivator, though as it weighed in at a mighty 15 tons it failed to find many applications. Enthusiasm was just as great in the United States, where rotary

RIGHT: The Clayton & Shuttleworth engine *Louise* going through her paces at the showground. The two operators share the workload: one driving and one steering.

cultivators were also tried. A patent was taken out for a rotating plough in 1857 by a certain Elisha Otis. Nothing much more was heard of that either, but a good deal was to be heard of Mr Otis, for that same year he installed his safety elevator in a four-storey building in New York, a device which was to make the skyscraper a practical proposition.

Trials continued, and it looked for a while as if a Briton was to win the Royal Agricultural Society prize after all. James Usher was an Edinburgh brewer who in 1849 patented a cultivator said to be capable of working a very respectable 7 acres (2.8ha) a day at less cost than a traditional plough team could turn one acre. The first model of 1851 was deemed a success and an improved version was built in 1855. Usher was ready to claim his prize. A full-scale trial was mounted at the Royal Show. The result was a disaster. The machine was just about able to move itself over the ground and the blades simply gave the soil a light stirring or, as the official report put it, produce 'a mild confusion'. The final summary could hardly have been more damning. At the end of the trial the condition of the ground was worse than it had been at the beginning. Usher had spent thousands of pounds of his own money only to see the whole enterprise end in failure. It did not stop others trying, but the truth was they were following the wrong path. The way forward lay not with the cultivator after all, but with the plough.

THE PACE OF CHANGE

Stories reached Britain throughout much of the nineteenth century of spectacular successes in other parts of the world. In France there was a machine that was said to be able to dig a deep trench one mile long in just an hour, and an even more extravagant claim was made for an American steam plough of 1838 which was alleged to turn 250 acres (100 ha) a day. Oddly, no one seemed to be able to give any clear idea of how these amazing machines worked. Meanwhile the serious business of making a real working machine went on. The main problem facing all engineers was that of designing a machine that would move the plough without itself doing unacceptable damage by compacting the ground under its own weight. John Heathcoat was a most unlikely entrant into the field, for his best-known success could hardly have been a greater contrast – not heavy, panting monsters turning clods of earth, but a machine to manufacture that most delicate of fabrics: lace.

He formed a partnership with an engineer, Josiah Parkes, and together they solved part of the problem, using a system of cable haulage to move the actual plough shares. But the engine itself was a monster, and a most curious one at that. It moved on four sets of caterpillar tracks, each based on 8-ft (2.4-m) diameter drive wheels. This undercarriage supported a platform holding the engine and winding drums. Metal straps were stretched out

on either side to anchor points, each one carrying a plough. When one was being hauled in one side, turning a furrow, the other was being dragged out to the anchor point ready to start its working run. One obvious disadvantage was that the vast carriage left an unploughed strip down the centre of the field. Nevertheless, there were high hopes for the machine, until it went for trial for the Highland Agricultural Society prize – the Scottish equivalent of the English award. This took place in Dumfries in 1837. It was not a complete failure, but it was not a success either. The Society deliberated and awarded £100 instead of the full £500, small compensation for the inventors who had sunk over £10,000 in the project.

The idea of using straps, cables or ropes to move the plough proved to be the one part of the design that it was possible to develop. The problem of how to move the winding drums still had to be solved. A Scotsman, Alexander MacRae, found himself in the one part of the world where the answer was there for the taking, on the sugar plantations of New Guinea. The sugar fields were divided up by irrigation canals – wide, deep and, most importantly of all, running parallel. These were tracks already laid down, not for traction engines but for boats. The result was unique, a floating system of ploughing based on engines fixed on barges, one holding the winding drum and engine, the other the fixed anchorage for the cable. From there, it was a logical step to think in terms of two engines to draw the plough back and forth, the only disadvantage being that not many farms in the rest of the world boasted a neat canal system. One thing, however, had been demonstrated – cable ploughing worked.

The way forward for more conventional arable land was getting clearer, and now progress was being made at a far greater pace. Lord Willoughby d'Estere was one of the more unlikely innovators who tried out a number of systems which were successful as far as they went. His first engine came not from one of the accepted traction engine builders, but from the Great Western Railway works at Swindon, and the designer was said to be none other than the chief engineer Daniel Gooch whose locomotive class, the Iron Dukes, proved their worth by remaining in service for nearly half a century. At least if you went to Gooch you were assured of quality and reliability. The system was, however, decidedly odd. At its heart was a portable wooden platform mounted on a temporary rail track and on top of this sat the engine. As in the Heathcoat and Parkes system it sat in between two ploughs connected by cable. As the working plough was drawn in, controlled by one man, the second was taken to the opposite side of the field by a horse. It was not an

RIGHT: John Fowler's name has an honourable place in the ranks of British manufacturers. This is a compound, with two steam cylinders visible behind the chimney.

ABOVE: Under particularly demanding farming conditions, America was to develop its own very distinctive range of traction engines. This early photograph shows an unnamed engine dating back to around 1890.

economical way of working – at best it reduced the number of horses, without eliminating them altogether. But the use of steel cables was shown to be effective, and this was tried at much the same time by John Williams who farmed at Baydon, Wiltshire – it can hardly be coincidence that this is just a few miles from the Great Western Railway works at Swindon. He was not just a practical engineer, he was also a great enthusiast and showed a typical Victorian love of statistics, even if they were not always based on verifiable figures. He worked out that the use of steam on the farm would release four horses for every acre of arable land and as there were said to be 47 million acres (19 million ha) under cultivation that would mean 1,880,000 redundant horses. From there he went on to work out how many other animals could be raised on the food no longer needed for horses and how much transport costs could be reduced. It was all done with a nice, if hopelessly unrealistic, accuracy. One does not need to have a

LEFT: An appreciative admirer inspects the attractive work of another highly successful manufacturer, a Ransom, Sims & Jeffries engine built in Ipswich, England.

degree in statistics to work out that an equation that starts with redundant horses and ends by concluding that Britain could now be expected to raise an extra 8,057,150 sheep has got lost somewhere down the line. But it all sounded most encouraging and inventors returned to the task with new enthusiasm, though Williams himself never produced anything more useful than dubious figures.

THE NEW STEAM PLOUGH

Just across the county border in Berkshire, another farmer called Hannam devised the 'Roundabout' system. Here at last was a steam ploughing method that was both simple and effective. The plough itself was attached to a continuous cable moved by a steam windlass. Directions of movement were controlled by a series of anchor points at the corners of the field and by intermediate supports or 'porters'. The beauty of this was that the plough could follow the edge of the field, no matter what its shape, a huge advantage in a country where large square fields were far from common. It had another advantage in that any portable engine could provide the power, and once ploughing

ABOVE: Canadian engines look very different from their British counterparts. This Waterloo engine from Ontario is notable for its rather flimsy looking front wheels and axle.

was over it could simply be set to other tasks. It was improved by the Fisken Brothers of Northumberland who used gearing on the plough, which enabled the rope to be moved at high speed while the plough itself could move slowly and steadily. Unlike so many of the other early ideas, the Roundabout made it into commercial production. It was not, however, destined to prove the final answer. That was provided by yet another Wiltshire man, John Fowler.

Although he started his working life with a local grain merchant, Fowler knew from an early age that his future lay elsewhere, so he took himself off to Yorkshire at the age of twenty one to join an engineering company. His first successful device

was not involved with ploughing but with the not too dissimilar problem of land drainage. The mole drain was aptly named, though the underground tunnel was created by a metal rather than a furry mole. Shaped like a small artillery shell, the mole had a vane on top which poked up through the surface so that

ABOVE RIGHT: An early American design, the so-called 'Walking Tractor', built by Henry B. McMurray of Pennsylvania, shown here in an 1885 advertisement.

BELOW RIGHT: A large American ploughing engine, displaying its fringed canopy and spark-arrester chimney, here being demonstrated around 1895.

ABOVE: A contemporary model of James Usher's patent steam plough of 1849. The full-scale trials that were held in 1855 were a complete and utter failure.

RIGHT: Darkness does not bring everything to an end at the steam fair. In this evocative picture, Marshall No 51025 steams proudly on through the night.

it could be dragged along to create its artificial burrow. Fowler's improvement was to use the same technique to draw along a set of tiles behind the mole to create an altogether more secure drain. He then went on to improve the system by means of cable haulage and a steam engine. The elements were all coming together. Fowler, still in his twenties, began to think about cable ploughing, and was astute enough to recognise the weakness in many early attempts. In these the plough had to be pulled out to the headland, doing no useful work along the way, before any actual ploughing could begin. So he set about devising a balanced plough, with two sets of ploughshares, one for working in one direction and one for the other, and so arranged that whichever was in use the furrows were always turned in the same direction. Like others, he began by using a single engine and anchor point, but quickly appreciated that a lot of time and effort could be saved by using two engines, one on each side of the field, and each fitted with its own winding drum so that they could work together. In 1858 the Royal Agricultural Society decided that its exacting standards had finally been met and the £500 prize was duly awarded. The cash was no doubt welcome, but it was the official seal of approval that really mattered and now engines could go into commercial production. At first, Fowler used a number of different manufacturers, but it was soon clear that a huge demand was developing. He set up a partnership with a production engineer, William Hewitson, and John Fowler and Co. of Hunslet, Yorkshire was born. They were to dominate the world of steam ploughing for as long as it remained in use. It is a story of great success, but without the

conventional happy ending, for Fowler died in 1864 at the age of 38, just when the world was beginning to appreciate what he had achieved.

The name John Fowler remains almost synonymous with ploughing engines, and not just in Britain, for Fowlers were sent throughout the world until production ceased in 1935. But it is as well to remember all the others who came before whose efforts contributed to the eventual solution of the problem, not to mention the inventive minds in quite different areas of technology who developed the steel cable, without which the whole system would have failed. There were others, such as Burrell, Aveling and Porter and McLaren, who proved successful builders of double-engine systems, but it is the Fowlers that everyone remembers, huge black engines, uncompromisingly powerful, almost brutal. The same system was quickly taken up in Europe and the German manufacturers Kemma produced ploughing engines that were, if anything, even more overwhelming than the Fowlers. In the later models, they even showed concern for the drivers by providing a canopy to keep off the worst of the weather.

The logic that brought specialist contractors into threshing also applied to ploughing. One of the biggest was Ward and Duke of Sleaford, Lincolnshire. In 1908 they had 24 pairs of engines with all the associated ploughing and cultivating gear, which represented a capital investment of well over £100,000. In the years just before World War II they could still regularly be seen – and they could certainly be heard – rumbling down country lanes. The unsprung, steel wheels set up an almighty clatter on the road as the convoy, consisting of the two ploughs,

RIGHT: The most successful form of steam plough was devised by John Fowler, using a pair of engines working together to pull the plough from one engine to the other.

BELOW: An early form of steam ploughing was the Roundabout, introduced in the 1850s. The plough was fastened to the cable which was guided round the field by pulleys.

VO·8988

water cart and living vans, came into view. There was generally a crew of five. This included two engine-drivers, a ploughman, a foreman, and a boy (who did all the dirty jobs no one else wanted to do). That sight is no longer with us, but the engines are and steam ploughing demonstrations are a regular feature at many fairs and rallies today.

WORKING THE MACHINES

The engines themselves seem at first glance to be identical. Each has a drum capable of holding 1,300–1,800ft (400–550m) of heavy cable, and it needs to be heavy to withstand some very tough wear as it is dragged out over rough, hard ground. There is, however, one important difference between the two: one is right-handed the other left-handed. In other words, one feeds the cable out to the right, its partner to the left, and they can be distinguished by the hefty cable arm sticking out from the side of the machine. Each arm ends in a pulley system, known as a 'monkey's head', although it has to be said a certain amount of imagination is needed to see any ape-like features. The drums themselves, situated beneath the boiler, are operated by simple gearing from the crankshaft, engaged by a lever operated by a dog clutch. A friction band on the drum keeps the speed under control. The engines themselves are bigger than the usual traction engine, and have always been noted for their large capacity boilers, which reduce the number of interruptions in the working day. They are compounds with a neatly arranged, steam-jacketed cylinder block. One essential piece of equipment is the steam whistle. When the two engines are aligned on the opposite sides of a big field they might not actually be in sight of each other, particularly in hilly country where a field might rise in the centre. But the drivers can always hear the whistle and see the plume of steam rising into the air. When alignment is complete, the plough is drawn across the field with one or even two men to control it, travelling at a brisk walking pace. One half will be in contact with the soil, the other half stuck up in the air. At the end of each furrow, the two engines advance just far enough for the next run to begin and the plough is tilted over, so that the share positions are reversed.

The machines were robust, but still required skilled handling and regular maintenance. Contractors soon realised that the best work would be obtained by giving the men on the team a financial incentive to keep everything in good order. Some gave a small bonus for every day the machines were at work, but nothing if one was taken out for repair. Others gave cash bonuses according to the acreage actually ploughed. One disadvantage of

LEFT: This photograph shows a 'left hand' ploughing engine. The cable drum can be seen beneath the boiler and the cable feeds out on the left through the 'monkey's head'.

the work as far as the teams were concerned was that, like all farm work, it was seasonal. Some of the best contractors gave the men long-term employment. They got a subsistence payment in the summer and that was offset by overtime payments when ploughing work was at its height. Overtime was hard earned, since the standard working day was already ten hours, but on the whole the system worked – good money for long hours balanced against minimum wages at other times, but with the opportunity for other paid work if available. The agricultural societies which had been such enthusiastic supporters of the

move to steam also did their bit by offering annual awards to the best engine men.

Those who know only the fields of Europe can have little conception of the vast fields of the North American prairie states. It is common to speak of 'prairie farming' in Britain to indicate the large grain fields that are now common in areas such as East Anglia, but even the biggest would be lost in the immensity of North America's prairies. Driving across western Canada, for example, it can seem that the whole country is just one vast grain field, with nothing to break the monotony but the

LEFT AND ABOVE: This pair of photographs shows German steam ploughing in operation. The 'right hand' engine can be seen, with the taut cable passing to the plough. The balanced plough is being pulled in, and the half now raised into the air will be lowered for the return journey, so that the furrows will always be turned in the same direction.

occasional eruption of tall grain silos on the horizon. In such country, thinly populated as it was in the nineteenth century, a machine had to earn its living. The bigger it was and the more work it could do, the better. Among the great manufacturers, Case was particularly noted for its big engines, including the 'single square', so called because it combined a 12-in (30-cm) diameter cylinder with a 12-in (30-cm) stroke. This gave a massive 110hp which in trials at the Winnipeg Industrial Exhibition of 1908 resulted in 32 acres (13ha) being ploughed in eight hours, and not only that but it impressed the cash-conscious farmers by using less fuel than its rivals.

Threshing and ploughing were the main uses for steam on the farm, but not the only ones. It should always be remembered that, efficient as it was, steam never completely vanquished the horse plough. A.G. Street, author of one of the best accounts of farming in the early years of the twentieth century, *Farmer's Glory* (Faber & Faber, 1932), described his father's farm in Wiltshire — an area which was one of the birthplaces of the steam revolu-

tion. He had 400 acres (160ha) of arable, not a vast area, but he kept six plough teams right up to World War I. Moving up in scale, a survey carried out in Kent in 1898 reported that there were 28,000 horses on farms in just that one county. Steam on the farm was by no means an all-conquering force: it was to prove even more difficult to establish steam on the road.

RIGHT: The enthusiasm for preserving agricultural engines is not confined to any one country. This gleaming engine was built by America's J.I. Case.

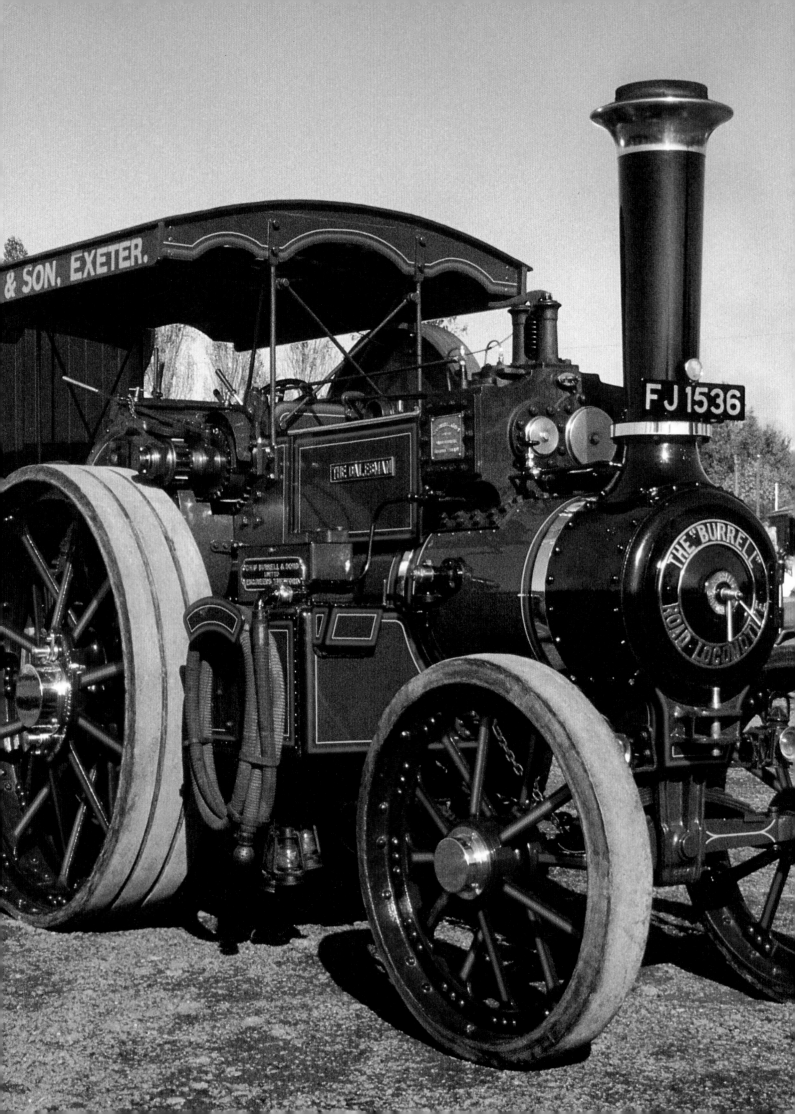

CHAPTER 3

ON THE ROAD

The Victorians had very few doubts about steam and transport: if you wanted to move passengers or goods around by steam then you set your engine down on rails. The growth of the railway system was phenomenal. The first line to use steam locomotives for both passenger and freight trains, the Liverpool and Manchester, was only opened in 1831 and was a mere 30 miles (48km) long, yet just forty years later railways had been opened to a greater or lesser degree on all five continents. Altogether there was by then almost 150,000 miles (241,500km) of track open for traffic and the system was still growing. This was very good news for all those with a vested interest in railways, although not everyone felt the same. What the railway companies had, they intended to keep. In Britain, the canal system, which had carried the traffic of the eighteenth-century Industrial Revolution, fell increasingly under railway ownership. It was usually a condition of purchase that the canal should not be closed, but there was nothing to say that it had to be kept busy.

ABOVE: The extraordinary Boydell engine of 1853, which overcame bad road surfaces by putting down its own 'track' as it moved – a forerunner of the caterpillar tractor.

LEFT: A Burrell on display at Toddington, England, in 1993. Unlike the agricultural engines, most road engines had protective canopies for the benefit of the crew.

With canal competition steadily increasing, only the roads remained as a potential rival. Obviously roads were needed. Rails could not reach everywhere and, if nothing else, roads were needed to bring passengers and freight to and from the station and goods yard. However, what was definitely not needed, in the view of all good railwaymen, was any system of long-distance transport other than their own. This was a view that was shared by those with responsibility for the roads, that odd mixture of local parishes and turnpike trusts. There might be a good case for establishing a steam haulage business on the road from, say, Birmingham to Manchester. It might well be of great value to companies at either end of the route, but it was of no interest at all to the road authority of some little village along the way who did not want to see metal-shod monsters adding to their repair bills. They were perfectly happy, however, for the goods to be sent by rail, where repair and track upkeep was entirely the responsibility of the London and North Western Railway.

The only way roads were going to be opened up to steam vehicles was with the active encouragement of the government, and because it was seen to be in the general interest. Parliament did have some responsibility for the turnpikes and set limits on tolls for all kinds of traffic. This did not include steam however, because when the regulations were drawn up nobody had even considered such a remote possibility. The trusts could charge

steam vehicles what they liked – and they did. It was not unusual for charges to be as much as 15 times as high for a steam
engine as they were for a similar load on a horse-drawn wagon.
Even Parliament realised that such demands were wholly unreasonable, and a Bill was passed by the House of Commons in
1836 to limit the charges levied on steam engines. But when it
reached the House of Lords, the conservative landed interest
threw it out and the road authorities were left to set whatever
rates they chose. That remained the situation until 1861 when
the Locomotive Act appeared. At first sight it looked like good
news for steam on the road since it did limit tolls at last, and it
was followed by a second Act of 1865 designed to clarify the
law. This was the famous, or infamous if you favoured mechanical transport, Red Flag Act. It specified that all road locomotives
should be attended by at least three people, one of whom had to
walk 60 yards in front carrying a red flag by day and a red

lantern at night. This was not really quite as bad as it sounds as
speeds were in any case restricted to 2mph (3.2km/h) in built-
up areas and 4mph (6.5km/h) on the open road – nevertheless,
the red flag man would have to have been pretty fit to keep
ahead of an engine trundling on at 4mph (6.5km/h). Other
clauses must have seemed common sense at the time. It was,
after all, only reasonable that highway authorities should not
allow loads that were too great for a bridge to bear.
Unfortunately, there was no attempt at defining how a bridge's
strength was to be assessed – and is it no more than coincidence
that many of the surviving cast-iron plates that ban locomotives
also have the name of a railway company as author of the ban?
To add insult to injury, if any bridge was damaged by a steam
vehicle, then the owner had to pay for the repairs, where other
road users did not. Small wonder that steam men such as
Thomas Aveling fulminated against the law:

LEFT: An impressive display of haulage power as a massive tree trunk is pulled along, mounted on a typical pole wagon that was specially designed for moving timber.

beast in case it annoyed their own. The law decreed that no engine could blow off its safety valve on the highway. This must have caused many an interesting dilemma. It is not surprising that with all these difficulties to overcome, even before mechanical problems could be addressed, there was little enthusiasm for steam haulage. The miracle is that there was any progress at all.

THE HAULAGE ENGINE

Advances came in Britain because the steam engine was steadily proving its worth, in rural districts at least. The sight of an engine lumbering down the road hauling a threshing set was becoming increasingly common, and whatever the alarmists might have said, horses were not bolting and dying of panic at the sight of them, any more than the cattle in a field by a railway were unduly disturbed by a train passing a good deal faster than any road engine could travel and blowing off as much smoke and steam as the driver desired. There were areas where the traction engine had a really useful role to play as a haulage engine, and nowhere more so than in forestry.

The Burrell-Boydell engine, that curious half-way stage between the conventional wheeled traction engine and the caterpillar tractor, made what was, if not the first, at least the first recorded run with a load of timber. It made its slow journey all the way from Thetford in Norfolk to Woolwich Arsenal in 1857. However, it was not as a long-range haulier that the traction engine was to make its mark, but in the heart of the forest itself. It transformed the work of felling, for example, in the removal of tree stumps – a tedious task when done by hand, but significantly easier with a machine and wire rope.

The engine proved most useful in removing the felled trunks from copse, wood or forest. This difficult job had previously fallen to the heavy horses, and of all the tasks they were required to do, this was about as bad as any. Not only were the loads enormous – the trunk of a mature tree could weigh several tons – but the conditions were bad as well. As anyone who has ever tried to walk along a bridleway through woodland will know, there is nowhere muddier, and nowhere as likely to stay muddy as the shade prevents the sun from reaching the ground after rain. Add to that the undergrowth, which can be anything from springy saplings and thorny brambles to sizeable rocks, and it is difficult to imagine worse conditions. The horses may well have had little problem with the load once they were set on a broad forest track: getting there in the first place presented the real problem. Happily, thorns and saplings mean little to traction engines, even if the same could not be said of rocks and mud.

If I send a boiler weighing fifteen tons drawn by fifteen horses (weighing eight tons) over a bridge and that boiler breaks the bridge, I have nothing to pay, but if I send the same boiler over the bridge drawn by an engine (weighing eight tons) and that boiler breaks through the bridge, I have the whole expenses to pay.
(*A Hundred Years of Road Rollers*, Aveling & Barford, 1965)

Equally harmless in intent but irksome in practice was the regulation that allowed local authorities to prohibit movement during certain hours which they were allowed to nominate. This could lead to the infuriating circumstance of one authority banning all movement by day while the adjacent authority banned all movement by night. Moreover, the Act bore the mark of the horse and carriage gentry concerned to pacify the mechanical

The worst jobs came when a huge log had to be moved from deep in the forest, perhaps for a kilometer or more. In really bad conditions, even getting the engine to the log could prove difficult. Modern tractors with their massive soft tyres can still dig deep ruts: the effect of the far heavier, steel-wheeled traction engine was even worse. If nothing else would work, the rope had to be led out to a suitably substantial tree and the engine would slowly wind itself forwards, in as many stages as necessary, until it reached the site. If the engine could not move itself by direct drive, it was certainly not going to move both itself and its load. In such a case, the engine had to be scotched, that is, secured to a tree and given extra solidity by baulks of timber against the wheels. Ropes were never attached directly for the wire would cut deep into the trunk and damage the timber. Instead chains were fastened round and it was these that were then hooked on to the wire tow rope. Ideally, a trunk would be dragged out top first to minimise damage to the ground, but where the lie of the land made that impossible the butt came first, gouging out a deep furrow as it came. The wire rope was hauled out away from the engine, hooked to the trunk and pulling could begin – one of those tasks that it is a good deal easier to talk about than actually to do. Sometimes not enough power was available, and blocks had to be used. Snatch blocks were preferred, which could be opened out and slid over the wire, a much easier operation than threading wire through a conventional block. This gave a mechanical advantage, but there was a price to pay. In a simple straight pull from the draw bar, if 14ft (4m) of wire are wound in, then the tree will also move 14ft (4m); with a single block the distance moved for the same amount of power is only 7ft (2m). It made for slow work. As it is not in the nature of forest floors to be smooth and even, a great deal of effort had to be put in with jacks, blocks and levers to get round and over obstacles.

Once out of the wood and into a suitable clearing, the logs could be loaded up. A special form of trailer was developed, variously known as a drag, tug, carriage or pole wagon. At the front was a steerable carriage, linked to the rear carriage by a long pole, hence the name 'pole wagon'. The timber was rested on a bolster, which had movable pins to keep the timber in place. The rear carriage could also be adjusted, and moved to different positions down the pole to suit the load being carried. To get the log up from the ground, the tug was positioned between the engine and the log, and skids, made of squared-up hardwood, were fixed in place against the bolster. This was no easy task when the skids themselves could weigh up to 200lb (90kg)

LEFT: It was sometimes more convenient to bring the saw mill to the log, rather than the log to the saw mill. A portable saw bench is demonstrated here, the belt being driven by the engine.

each. Chains were fixed round the log and again fastened to a hook on the wire rope from the engine. The slack was taken up and the log began its slow journey up the skids. It all required precise positioning for everything to run smoothly, and there were often pauses while fine adjustments were made to ensure the essential easy movement. It demanded a lot of skill from the men, and a lot of hard work from the engine. The straight spruce, so common in modern forestry plantations, would have presented few problems and the job would have been quickly concluded. An old, misshapen oak would pose a real challenge and demand the most careful handling.

Even with the load safely secured, the difficulties were far from over. There would still be a great deal of manoeuvring and rope haulage before the load was out of the wood for a comparatively easy passage on a proper road. Steering a traction engine down a country lane can seem daunting enough to the beginner. A road which might have seemed reasonable enough before, suddenly seems to shrink when viewed down the full length of an engine boiler. Bends become impossible contortions and are preferably treated with due caution, providing the amateur steerer can persuade the driver to slow down. One can only guess now at the problems involved when a tug with logs weighing perhaps 10 tons and perhaps 30ft (10m) long is attached behind you.

A long, heavy load, such as timber, did not just present the obvious practical problems of manoeuvrability: the load could seem to have a life of its own. Weighing more than the engine doing the pulling, it gained momentum as it moved. Even on the flat, it could seem to be pushing the driver along at a rate faster than he really wanted to go. The effect became even more

pronounced on downhill sections – on steeper hills someone would have to be despatched to operate the brakes on the carriage. Any slope, up or down, involved a change of gear, an operation which itself called for some skill and accurate timing. Steering round sharp bends produced yet more problems, for the front end of the tug, with its moveable carriage, had wheels following one curve, while the fixed wheels at the back would be following another. The steerer generally had to rely on long experience and lessons learned from early mistakes. No one starts off as an expert, and in the learning period a steerer could demolish a good deal of roadside furnishings and fixings with just one swing of the rear end of a tug. The final test of skill came at the timber yard, which was usually a small space with not much room for manoeuvre. Fortunately, there was generally a crane of some sort, possibly even a crane engine, to help with

the unloading. Even so, manoeuvring could be a nightmare: going in was bad enough, but backing out even worse. Prudent drivers often preferred to unhitch the tug and manhandle it out of the yard. As Geoff Gilbert, who knew the trade well, wrote: 'The experiences gained at timber hauling are not readily forgotten [surely a considerable understatement] when the limitations of the tackle are considered in relation to present-day equipment, the activities of these little engines and the men who drove them seem all the more remarkable' (quoted in *Steam is the Essence*, R.A. Whitehead, 1993, published by the Road Locomotive Society). Indeed they do.

Life is easier when the saw mill is brought to the log, rather than the other way round. Indeed, the portable saw mill had its place in forestry, mostly being used to provide the most basic, but essential items, such as fence posts. As with farm machinery, the saw mill was run by belt drive from the engine. Most of these portable mills would give a modern safety inspector apoplexy. There was no guard on the belt drive nor, more alarmingly, was there any protection from the rotating saw blade. Timbers were fed in by hand with apparent nonchalance. I once asked an old saw mill operator if the work was dangerous – as a reply, he held up his hands, which displayed rather less in the way of fingers than one normally expects to find.

A VERSATILE MACHINE

Another area of heavy haulage which made extensive use of steam was stone quarrying, and its introduction was a merciful relief to the horses whose life was even harder than those working in forestry. It was punishing to the point of cruelty. The Reverend J. Skinner visited the famous quarries on the Isle of Portland in 1804 and described the work in harrowing terms. The stone wagons were mainly employed in taking the stone blocks from the quarries at the top of the cliffs to the harbour at the foot, and this involved harnessing one horse at the front and two behind, and it was the pair at the rear that suffered most.

They squat down on their haunches and suffer themselves to be dragged for many yards, struggling with all their strength against the weight that forces them forwards. To one unaccustomed to the sight, it appears as though their limbs must inevitably be dislocated, or their sinews cracked by the violence of their exertions.
(from the MS Journal, 18 September 1804)

LEFT: This American engine, *Peerless*, dates back to the 1890s. It is notable for the very high dome above the boiler that gives it the look of a small railway locomotive.

ABOVE: A marine boiler being moved on a crude trolley at the boiler works owned by the Riley Brothers, one of whom was the author's great grandfather, at Stockton-on-Tees, northeast England.

'Boy' Male was born and brought up on Portland, a rugged island in southern England, and he recently described the scene to me as he remembered it from the 1920s.

My childhood reverberated to the sound of thundering fifteen-ton steam traction engines hauling their eight-ton trucks of block stone noisily past our very doorstep. Our roads, pitted by the continual daily use of the great steel-slatted engine wheels, were a quagmire in winter and ankle-deep in dust all summer.

The engines he remembered would often have been war surplus, bearing suitably military names, which included *Kitchener* and *Jellicoe*. The work they faced was not so very different from that of the horses – and no less dangerous. In slippery conditions, drag shoes were used, wooden wedges placed in front of the wheels of the cart to slow progress. Even so, accidents happened, often due to mechanical failure. In July 1921, a pin broke on the wheel of George White's engine. It careered down the hill at Fortuneswell on the Isle of Portland, and the unfortunate driver was crushed to death by his load. But in their time, the engines did splendid work – even if the road repair bills were

enormous – right up to 1931 when the last engine was retired. All that remains as a reminder of those days, is one old steam engine quietly rusting away near Portland Bill at the tip of the island.

Although these were the major uses of traction engines, throughout Britain there were important jobs to be done. It might seem that the railways had solved all transport problems once and for all, but as promoters soon discovered, taking branch lines into rural areas was expensive, and the expense was never likely to be covered by passenger and freight payments. Canals still had a role to play, and coastal shipping was of major importance, but for many communities the horse and cart remained the norm. Loads were limited, and distances that could be travelled would scarcely exceed 9 miles (15 km). Beyond that there were extra costs to bear, such as stabling. Huge quarry blocks represented just one variety of load, and there was also a big demand for smaller stones for all kinds of purposes, of which road making and repair were far from the least important. This was particularly true for areas where stone was not readily available, for example, in a good deal of East Anglia in eastern England. The more engines took over the work of the horse and carriage, the less daunting they appeared and the more absurd the scare stories of the 1840s

ABOVE: Unlike the more modest Riley Brothers, mighty Harland and Wolff, builders of the Titanic, are shown here using a team of six powerful horses to move an impressively sized boiler.

were shown to be. Richard Tangye, one of the more important figures to emerge during what might be called the rebirth of steam on the roads, noted in his autobiography (published 1869) that 'a judge ruled that a horse that would not stand the sight or sound of a locomotive, in these days of steam, constituted a public danger, and that its owner should be punished and not the owner of the locomotive. In this case, sadly, the judiciary proved more radical than the legislature.' In spite of the difficulties, the demand for steam traction was growing and would not be denied. It had seemed in the 1840s that all hopes of steam haulage becoming a regular feature on British roads had died; but they were not dead, merely dormant. By the 1860s, interest had revived and the traction engine and its natural successors, the steam tractor and steam wagon, were to play an important role in transport for another fifty years.

Traction engines proved their worth over and over again in many specialised areas, but what was considered suitable for remote country areas was not necessarily welcomed elsewhere. Yet the Industrial Revolution that had given birth to the traction engine had not come to a halt. The industrial world was still expanding, not just producing more things than ever before, but bigger things as well – things that sometimes had to be transported from one place to another. One area where this was

notably true was in shipbuilding. Steam had been accepted as an efficient method of moving vessels through water a good deal earlier than it had been accepted on land, and as the nineteenth century wore on, so the steam ship came to dominate the oceans of the world. The use of an iron hull made it possible to build far larger vessels than had ever been possible with wood, and as the ships grew bigger so everything associated with them grew bigger as well. It was a process that continued right through the nineteenth century and into the twentieth, a time which saw the development of the great ocean liners. Where everything was manufactured and assembled on one site, transport was not a problem, but where elements had to be brought in from outside manufacturers this was a very different matter. Surprisingly perhaps, given the huge technological changes in the shipbuilding industry, horses still had a part to play. One famous photograph shows an anchor for the Titanic leaving the forge at Dudley in central England, drawn by no fewer than twenty horses. The most common element to be sent from specialist manufacturers to the shipyard was the boiler. The sheer size of the ship's boiler meant that it could not be sent by rail – even if special trucks had been built it would never have passed through stations without demolishing a good part of the structure – and so long, overland journeys had to be made. It does come as something of a shock, however, to find what we would now regard as the hi-tech companies of the day, such as Harland and Wolff, still relied on the horse to move boilers, even in the early twentieth century. My great grandfather was one of the Riley Brothers who manufactured marine boilers at Stockton-on-Tees in northeast England, and works photographs show traction engines in regular use. Family pride in such modernity is slightly dented, however, when one notices the crudeness of the trolleys on which the boilers, towering high above the engines themselves, are carried.

A BUMPY RIDE

One thing that became evident was that if engines were going to spend more time on the roads, rather than just making short trips between jobs, as the farm engines did, they would have to be adapted for the task. Changes would have to be made to the engines themselves, for it was very clear that no one was going to improve the roads to suit them. Many manufacturers applied themselves to the first important job, of providing some form of springing. Foden, the English manufacturers who were later to become famous as makers of steam wagons, proudly showed off the results of their labours by advertising their product with these words:

*This perfect spring arrangement materially reduces the
effect of shocks or vibrations caused by passing over rough roads,
and it is conducive to the reduction of the wear and tear arising
from such causes in ordinary traction engines, as leaky fire-boxes,
tubes and joints, strained frames, and the jolting to pieces of the
motion work throughout. Moreover, this spring-mounting
arrangement adds very considerably to the comfort
of the engine-driver and steerer.*

One cannot help feeling that the line about the comfort of the men came as something of an afterthought, but the list of horrors perpetrated by bad roads at least makes it clear why springing was given such careful consideration.

The problem of springing does not appear at first to be that difficult, as the use of springs on all kinds of road carriages dates back to the seventeenth century, and indeed it was easily solved on the first generation of chain-driven engines. The introduction of geared drives was a different matter. Any movement of the drive axle could affect the meshing of the gears, if some compensation was not made. All kinds of solutions were produced, some very elaborate and fanciful, some rather crude but quite practical. Perhaps the most successful was a system patented by Fowler in 1892. A strong, steel plate spring supported the

weight at the rear, and an equalising arrangement ensured that any up and down movement in the spring was always at right angles to the rear axle, ensuring that the gears ran true. A simple laminated spring above the front axle allowed freedom of movement as the engine bumped its way down what was often a hopelessly inadequate road. American manufacturers generally preferred different arrangements. Case, for example, used a system whereby the entire weight of the engine rested on spiral springs which permitted the whole boiler to rise up and down, while simple link connections kept the gearing perfectly in train. This was only a part of the battle to achieve a smoother ride, and it was clear that the work the springs were required to do could be reduced if there was less bumping around at the contact between wheels and road. So if the road was not going to be improved, perhaps something could be done about the wheels.

Various methods of softening the impact of the wheels on the road were attempted, including setting wooden blocks around the rims. The eventual solution had its origins in the work of Charles Goodyear, a hardware manufacturer from Philadelphia, who took out a patent in 1841 for a new process for hardening rubber, which became known as vulcanisation. He applied for an English patent in 1843, but was beaten to the post by a local man Thomas Hancock, who had quite independently been working on a similar idea. But at least there was now a new material available that might be applied to transport. Robert Thompson, a British inventor, took out a patent for a pneumatic tyre in 1845. This consisted of an inner tube made up of a large number of air sacs of rubberised calico, held in place by an outer case of canvas and leather. It was not a success, but he went on to try a simpler version in which wheels were simply covered by indiarubber. That also failed. Thompson, however, was not a man to give in easily. The biggest problem he had to overcome was that the rubber was too soft, so that on really hot days driving with rubber-tyred wheels was a bit like trying to drive through glue. Nevertheless he kept trying and in the 1850s he designed what he described as a 'light' steam tractor – it actually weighed in at about 5 tons – which could be used for road haulage. Its novel feature was its indiarubber tyres. The softening problem might have been reduced, however, but a new one now appeared. The rubber stretched, so that the combination of a warm day and muddy ground could see the wheels merrily spinning round inside immobile tyres. Even this did not deter Thompson – it is doubtful if anything could deter him – and he hit on the idea of encasing the rubber tyre in armour, an outer casing of steel plates. The idea never caught on in Britain, but Thompson found a market for his three-wheeled tractors with armoured tyres in other parts of the world, from Greece to India. Perseverance had finally paid off and the success brought a new partnership for Thomas Burrell, a manufacturer from Thetford in Norfolk, who took up the idea. One of the problems with the Thompson tractor had been the design of the vertical boiler, and Burrells soon replaced this with a more conventional, horizontal, railway-type boiler. It was not, however, the vertical boiler as such that was the problem, but Thompson's version of it. At much the same time as he was working on his engine, Lotz had designed a three-wheeled tractor, also with vertical boiler, which was put to work in Paris. And where Thompson and Burrell had led, others followed, and in time a hard-wearing, solid-rubber tyre became standard on all but the heaviest engines.

The long-range, heavy haulage business brought in both specialist manufacturers and specialist carriers. The main British manufacturers were, in descending order of importance, Fowler, Burrell, Foster and McLaren, though Burrell was actually first in the field with a haulage engine on offer in 1856. The standard engines were 8hp, although 6-hp and 10-hp engines were also produced. Virtually all were compounds and three-speed, though 'speed' is not a word that one readily associates with these lumbering giants. The new engines also required specially

designed wagons if they were to work to their full potential. The boiler trolley mentioned earlier was a crude affair with tiny, solid wheels, but by the end of the steam age much more sophisticated road vehicles were on the market. Really heavy loads were placed on well-wagons. These had double bogies, each consisting of two or even three axles and capable of moving independently for easy steering. The notable hauliers were also few in number, dominated by the two Boxes, Norman Box of Manchester and Edward Box of Liverpool, the Kerrs of Glasgow, the Coupe Brothers of Sheffield and Pickfords of Cheshire. The latter eventually added to their share of the market by buying up both Norman Box and Coupe Brothers. In their time, these firms undertook some prodigious assignments.

One of the few places where one can still gauge the work done in Britain in the old days is Winchester, where a grand statue of King Alfred stands, brandishing his sword high over the city streets. Handsome as he is, it is not the bronze figure that

BELOW: A steam wagonette by Catley and Ayres, built in 1868. The owners do not look overjoyed at the thought of driving the ungainly and awkward-looking contraption.

concerns us here, but the 40-ton tall granite plinth on which he stands, and the 20-ton block on which the plinth itself rests. Quarried in Cornwall, the stone was hauled all the way to Hampshire by two Fowler engines, This was not a straightforward harnessing-up, but a fore and aft arrangement, with the front engine pulling and the rear engine acting as a brake for downhill sections. It was occasionally moved to the front for stiff climbs. This must have been an incredible journey in the days when by-pass was not even a word in the dictionary. When the statue was unveiled in 1901 it is doubtful if anyone gave much thought to the engine men who had ensured it rested on sound foundations.

The really hard work, however, came with the spread of electrical power in the early twentieth century. Immense accumulators were taken by road as single items and it speaks volumes for the power of the traction engine that such immense weights, not to mention such hugely unwieldy objects, could be taken at all on the roads of the day. The honour of carrying the biggest load with a single engine goes to a Fowler engine, of what was known as the 'Super Lion' class, on this occasion No. 1705 *Atlas*. The distance was a little over 80 miles (130km), from Annan to Glasgow, but the accumulator on its own weighed 90 tons, to which perhaps another 25 tons could be added for trailer and equipment. The speed was necessarily low, never rising to more than a modest walking pace, but the result was a success for the team and their willing Fowler.

AN EPIC JOURNEY

A Fowler engine featured again in what is now seen as the great epic journey of the steam age. The client was once again Cochran and Co. of Annan, who had established their boiler works in the town in 1898, and where two of their huge boilers are still preserved. The load was a steam accumulator, which was 70ft (21m) long and 12ft (3.5m) diameter. The destination was Beckton gas works in London's dockland, 325 miles (525km) away and the hauliers were Pickfords. This was not just a matter of dropping Pickfords a line to ask if they would mind popping over to pick up rather a large load for London. The preparations were put in hand a full 18 months before the load was due to set off. The first requirement was to travel over the whole route to look for problems – town streets that were too narrow, bridges that were too weak and so on. After that it was a question of liaising with the local authorities along the way, and in some cases special arrangements had to be made to strengthen bridges and to remove obstacles. The police were involved, just as they are today

RIGHT: The biggest challenge facing the traction engine came from the internal combustion engine, developed in Germany. Here a German traction engine stands by its diesel rival.

when an exceptional load has to be moved by road. A special trolley was supplied by Crane of Dereham, Norfolk, carried on two bogies each with 16 wheels. As the day approached, a second survey of the route was made to check that all necessary strengthening work had been carried out. Then, on 6 January 1938, the accumulator began its journey.

The Fowlers entrusted with pulling the beast were *Ajax* once again with 16263 *Talisman* and 16264 *Jix* pulling the crew's living van and helping out with braking and steering when needed. It was scarcely the best time of year for such an enterprise, but the convoy duly set out at a stately 2mph (3.5km/h). All went well until the famous – though the crew probably had

other names for it – Shap Fell was reached in the Lake District; with a summit of around 1,500ft (450m) this is among the bleakest of windswept moorlands, and beyond it lay a long steep descent towards Kendal. Here, just to add to the already formidable problems, the team encountered snow and *Jix* was kept busy helping to manage the slithering load. After that the procession made steady progress towards London. There was no way in which it was going to be allowed to disrupt the life of the city, so all the haulage had to be done by night, and to get it through with the minimum disruption the speed was stepped up to a sprightly 3mph (5km/h). Even so, it must have been an extraordinary sight as it passed through the capital, with the

LEFT: It is easy to see why the railways fought steam on the road: here an impressive train of road wagons being hauled by an Aveling and Porter c. 1890 is shown.

Pickfords had begun as a family concern in the early eighteenth century, based at Paynton in Cheshire, where their trade was based on heavy wagons, each drawn by at least six horses with a seventh kept in reserve for long journeys. They were quick to appreciate the advantages offered by the developing canal system, and bought their first boat in the 1770s. By 1820 they had a fleet of eighty boats with 400 horses to pull them. Then came the first railways, and once again they saw the way the world was moving and by 1847 they had sold off the last of their boats. But the railways proved too inflexible to meet all their needs, and they were soon back where they started – on the road. They began to develop a side of the business with which they have been associated ever since – furniture removals.

HOME HELP

It seems odd today to think of calling up a traction engine to help you move house, but when one considers the alternatives on offer a century or so ago, it makes perfect sense. The standard vehicle that had been developed for the trade was the pantechnicon, a word with almost as curious and convoluted an origin as Pickfords themselves. It originally referred to a bazaar full of works of art, and was adapted to mean any general store for furniture which could then be served by a pantechnicon van. Finally, the word 'van' was dropped, and so a bazaar became a vehicle. It was a simple high-sided, four-wheeled wagon with a low floor. On short runs it was worked by one or two horses, but for longer runs it was so designed that it could be carried by rail. Unless the movers were very well off, this meant consigning their precious possessions to a goods train, which in those days would have been loose coupled, the wagons fastened to each other by stout chains. The links were taut enough while the train was moving along, but at each stop the trucks barged up against each other in a succession of juddering bangs, and at each restart they were brutally yanked apart again. The effect on tea chests packed with china scarcely needs considering. The traction engine therefore proved ideal, and it was able to haul two or three pantechnicons with ease. The Fowler 8hp was very popular, though even the smaller 6hp could handle most jobs.

Pickfords may be the best known in the British furniture business today, but in the last century one of the busiest companies was Lalonde Brothers and Parham of Weston-super-Mare. They were enthusiastic users of steam, and the Lalondes were founder members of the National Traction Engine Owners Association. They famously fell out with Fowlers over a detail of the firebox design. They wanted it made slightly longer, but

police attendants and a newcomer in the form of a 3,000-gallon (13,650-litre) water tank, which was used to top up the boilers on the engines. The final destination was reached 21 days after leaving Scotland. It had been hard work for the men – Shap Fell in January on an open engine could hardly be described as travelling in comfort. There were many problems to overcome along the way. Often the crews had to lay down metal sheets to move the load round sharp bends and it was not uncommon to have to stop to cut down overhead branches or to rearrange wayside banks in the course of the journey.

The big loads were the spectacular side of the business, but there were more everyday matters to occupy the hauliers as well.

Fowlers flatly refused to modify their design. So Lalondes went off to Garrett, who produced a made-to-measure design in 1908, known as the Garrett No.6 Express or the Garrett-Lalonde. The hauliers soon began to regret interfering in engineering matters, for the new Garrett was not a success, suffering from overheating and cracked crankshafts. They were forced to return rather shamefacedly to Fowler and the whole affair cost them a good deal of money, particularly as at the end it all had to be handed over to lawyers to arrange a settlement.

RULES OF THE ROAD

Almost every aspect of travel on the roads was different in those days. The rules of the road did not demand that traffic stayed on one side or the other, merely, as far as Britain was concerned, suggested a move to the left when another vehicle was approaching. This was largely ignored by the furniture removers and their train of pantechnicons. Their preferred means of travel was straight down the middle. This did not mean that they were selfish road hogs, simply that with an extensive camber it was much safer to keep the wheels on each side of the crown to avoid sliding down into a roadside ditch in wet or icy weather. Controlling the little procession was, in any case, quite a complex affair, with the rearmost van performing much the same role as the brake van on the railways. Communication between front and back was usually no more than a piece of string which led from the steerer's arm to the young lad at the back, with signals for everything from applying the brakes to jumping down to inspect hot wheel bearings. The lad also had the least popular jobs and was always first to start the day, clearing out the fire, cleaning the boiler tubes and topping up with water before the more exalted steerer and driver put in an appearance. It was not an easy life, but then nothing involved with steam haulage ever was easy, but the men made the most of it. And for the more adventurous there were always means of shortening the journey time to gain an extra hour in the pub. One Lalonde driver recalled being overtaken on a hill in Kent while travelling with two vans by a colleague who also had two vans hauled by a similar engine. The speed merchant was rushing downhill with the engine out of gear and the brakes off. It was not something he would have liked the bosses to hear about.

It is interesting to compare the repressive legislation in Britain with government attitudes in the rest of Europe. The French government not only looked favourably on steam, but actually ordered three big McLaren engines for the postal service in 1886. They were set to work on the 70-mile (113-km) run

RIGHT: The Burrell Patent engine. One of the great improvements that was of potential benefit to all traction engines in the twentieth century was the introduction of rubber tyres.

ABOVE: A German Kemna heavy road locomotive complete with laden wagons. The rough-stone setts that form the surface of the road must have made for a particularly uncomfortable ride.

between Lyon and Grenoble, a journey which would not have been possible with British speed restrictions. But the French laws allowed the machines to bowl along at speeds of up to 8mph (12km/h), so that they could easily make the trip in a single day. This excellent service remained in use for many years. Not all European efforts were so successful.

A similar service was set up in Germany between Pirmasens and Speyer, and the authorities were determined that the enterprise should not fail for want of power. The engine ordered from Tuxford in 1863 looked, and in effect was, like two engines joined together side by side, with two boilers sprouting two chimneys. It lasted less then three months. But even in Britain, the tide was slowly turning towards greater freedom of movement for mechanical vehicles, even if it seemed to be moving at the speed of a light engine with a heavy load. In America there were quite different constraints on development. Distances were vast, there was no trunk-road system until well into the twentieth century and country districts often had only the flimsiest of wooden bridges. As a result, any runs that were allowed by the state of the roads required immense machines, such as the three-wheelers built by Daniel Best in California at the end of the nineteenth century. In any case, by the time the roads had been improved to the point where long-range haulage became feasible the traction engine was already being superseded by the truck with an internal combustion engine.

PASSENGER SERVICE

There remained one other obvious use for the steam engine on the road – moving passengers. In Britain, all attempts had been brought to a halt by the dead hand of legislation, but that hand did not reach across the whole of the British Empire. India was

to be the scene of one of the most ambitious of all such schemes. It began with a young officer in the Rifle Brigade, who boasted the resounding name of Rookes Evelyn Bell Crompton. In 1861, while he was still a schoolboy at Harrow, he designed and had built a primitive steam carriage, the *Bluebelle*, an interesting vehicle with a vertical boiler at the back and with a chain drive to one of the rear wheels. Two years later he left school at the age of 18 to work at the railway engineering works at Doncaster, where he improved his engine. After a short stay he abandoned the commercial world for the army and set off for India, with *Bluebelle* as part of his baggage. While in India he heard of Thompson's experiments with rubber tyres and thought they might improve the running of his road carriage. From this small beginning a far grander scheme was hatched by the two men: the Government Steam Train. The development of a railway system in India was only moving forward very slowly, but the recently completed Grand Trunk Road, linking Delhi to the Punjab, offered the opportunity to set up a road train service and the army backed the idea.

The first engine, *Chenab*, was built by Ransome of Ipswich in 1871, and one of the problems that beset all Thompson's own designs soon appeared – the inefficient boiler. This was a matter of some importance as in India the engine would not be run on good steam coal but on wood. Initial trials were not encouraging, so it was decided to increase the blast to the fire and run a full-scale trial on Ipswich racecourse. The increased blast was not just effective, it was too effective – red hot cinders flew from the chimney with the disastrous result that the main grand stand was set on fire. Other, less damaging, improvements were tried. An account of a later run as part of a general traction engine demonstration appeared in *The Engineer* (1871) and it shows something of Crompton's cavalier approach to steam and life in general. After only 5 miles (8km) the team found that they needed water so they stopped by an old lady's garden and got out the pump:

The hose was then popped into the old lady's well, without asking her consent. In a minute a good stream was pouring into our tank, and it was not until we had got all the water required that our confiding hostess found that we had pumped her well dry. After this discovery it became expedient that we should proceed as quickly as possible...

At 8.15 we passed Burrell's locomotive ... and availed ourselves of the opportunity to extinguish the lagging of Chenab's boiler, which had taken fire at the smokebox. Thompson's pot boiler is the best I ever saw for burning off lagging ... I may add here that the way in which Lieut. Crompton took his engine over heaps of stones by the roadside and into complicated holes and trenches when passing other engines was sufficient to startle weak nerves. I began to think that the Chenab had been designed pour la chasse.

It makes the whole thing sound like the worst kind of amateur enterprise, but it did at least have one positive outcome – it convinced Crompton that a whole new boiler was needed and the second engine *Ravee* was provided with the far more efficient Field boiler. This time Crompton planned a far more demanding trial, a run from Ipswich up to Edinburgh and back, and being on official government business he was not obliged to obey the speed regulations. As a result, in his own account of the trial he wrote that, 'though our loaded train weighed over forty tons, we were making speeds well over twenty – probably nearer thirty – miles an hour.' At one point he had the satisfaction of overtaking a goods train on the adjoining railway. He also had an opportunity on passing the house of the Director-General of the Indian Post Office at Lockerbie, to demonstrate the engine's ability to power up a 1:17 hill with a full load. The experiment was a triumph, the Government Steam Train was duly established with Crompton as official Superintendent. It was, however, destined

BELOW: Kemna produced engines that were both powerful and versatile. This nineteenth-century engraving shows an engine advertised as suitable for road haulage and agriculture.

Die Dampfmaschine

Grundlegend für das wirtschaftliche Arbeiten der Dampfmaschine

to have a short life. In 1875 the decision was taken to start building metre gauge railways to fill in the gaps in the Indian network and the road train was pensioned off.

Crompton's run showed just what steam on the roads could do once restrictions were removed, but restrictions were not going to be removed, and most experiments were ended for reasons that had nothing at all to do with failures in technology. Even so, there was still an interest in passenger vehicles. Thomas Rickett of Birmingham built an extraordinary engine, clearly influenced by railway locomotive design, except that it appeared to be going permanently in reverse, for the chimney was at the back and the driver with up to three passengers were seated in front of the boiler. The stoker had to make do with a small

platform at the back. It had a chain drive, weighed a ton and a half and was capable of speeds up to 12mph (19km/h), which must have made steering very hard work, since this was all done by a tiller to the front wheel. This was soon followed by a 5-tonner built by Carrett, Marshall and Co. of Leeds which could take up to nine passengers and had a spur-gear drive instead of a chain. One of the early customers who bought a Carrett was George Salt, the philanthropic textile magnate of Saltaire, a small town in northern England. Dismayed by official restrictions on its use, he gave it away to a steam enthusiast Frederick Hodges who named it *Fly-by-Night*, since that was the only time he dared try it out. Even so, six prosecutions in six weeks dampened even his ardour. In such circumstances it is hardly

Dion and Léon Serpollet both developed steam tricycles, but a much more important development was the first steam car to be produced by the Stanley Brothers of Newton, Massachusetts, in 1897. Important as they are in terms of the story of steam on the road as a whole, these creations scarcely qualified as traction engines. These developments, however, did affect the main line of development and we shall be returning to them later.

Meanwhile British legislation began to stagger out of the nineteenth century, encouraged by the growing numbers of steam users, who began to band together to make their voices heard. This started with the Kent County Engine Owners Association and eventually led to the formation of the National Traction Engine Owners and Users Association in 1893. The Association received the active support of all the leading manufacturers – J.E. Ransome, Thomas Aveling, John McLaren, R.H. Fowler, Charles Burrell and Edwin Foden were all present at the inaugural meeting. One of the first actions was to appoint a legal adviser, William Joynson-Hicks, universally known as 'Jix' (whose name was used for the traction engine that took part in the epic Annan to Beckton run). He was soon hard at work, marshalling evidence to present to a Parliamentary Select Committee, and he did his work well, the first results appearing in the Locomotives on Highways Act of 1896 which finally removed the need for the lookout man to walk in front and raised the speed limit for light traction engines to 6mph (10km/h). A second Act of 1898 raised the limit in built-up areas to 3mph (5km/h) and eased the tax burden on engines. To satisfy local authorities, there was a provision for engine owners to pay repair bills caused by 'extraordinary traffic'. Defining 'extraordinary traffic' was to keep lawyers in fees for many years.

Enforcing the regulations presented its own problems. In 1907, a driver in Tonbridge was seen to be breaking the law by making excess smoke in the centre of the town. The engine was, in fact, almost lost in a smoke screen, but enough was visible for the local police sergeant to take down its number, after furious whistle blowing and arm waving had been ignored, or possibly passed unseen. When the case came to court, the sergeant was asked why he did not chase after the engine, to which he memorably replied: 'The engine can go five miles an hour and I can only go two.' The court found the answer hilarious, which greatly grieved the good sergeant. 'A sergeant could not go up High Street in uniform at five miles an hour without bringing everyone out into the street' (quoted in *The Age of the Traction Engine*, R. Whitehead, 1970). This must have given great encouragement to all fleet-of-foot criminals in Tonbridge, who could be quite

surprising that the development of passenger transport eventually passed elsewhere.

In France Amadée Bollée of Le Mans built a steam passenger coach in 1880. It was quite unlike anything built in Britain, with an efficient two-cylinder engine mounted ahead of the front axle, with drive passing to the rear axle via a propellor shaft and bevel gearing, an arrangement very similar to that in the modern motor car. The stoker fed a boiler mounted at the rear, while the driver at the front had the advantage of a steering wheel, and in between was a comfortable coach for passengers. The success of engines such as this was a real encouragement, and designers in France, Germany and America began to think in terms of a new age of personal transport. In 1887 in France, the Comte de

ABOVE: Although the British firm Fowler, of Leeds, is probably best known for their big ploughing engines, they also built a wide range of tractors and general-purpose engines. Pictured here is one such engine, built around 1917.

sure of evading arrest. But prosecutions were not really a laughing matter, since the old prejudices of the local gentry who sat on the bench as magistrates remained fully in place. As the magistrate of the Hythe County Bench bluntly said when trying a case in 1907, 'traction engines are horrible things', thus giving the unfortunate owner a clear idea of which way the verdict was liable to go.

The new legislation did more than ease the difficulties for vehicle owners. By making a distinction between light and heavy engines, it opened up a whole new area for development, and further easing of regulations for light engines did even more to increase the enthusiasm of manufacturers. One line of development led to the widespread production of what came to be known as tractors, and provided they weighed less than 5 tons, they were permitted to dash along at 5mph (8km/h) with just one man in charge. Early 5-tonners were mostly single-cylinder with two or sometimes three speeds, but with the low weight

came small boiler capacity, and it was quickly realised that compounds that would use steam more effectively were preferable. These machines could travel about twenty kilometers without taking on water and carried enough coal to cover even longer distances, making them very handy for short hauls in towns. Specialist builders, such as Wallis and Steevens of Basingstoke, produced very small engines, weighing just 3 tons, but which were still capable of useful work. They proved particularly popular with brewers. Design details were altered to suit the engines to town use, including replacing the spoked flywheel with a solid wheel and covering in the motion, so that the engine appeared less daunting than the familiar traction engine and was accepted by even the most nervous horses.

The twentieth century saw more slackening of the rules in Britain. Tractors of up to 7.5 tons were permitted in 1923. The traction engine had now reached its final stage of development, and there were to be no more fundamental changes in its design. The last generation worked at high pressure and had more power than they were generally permitted to use – even when the speed limit was raised to 12 miles (20km) an hour, the engines were well able to surpass it. Manufacturers such as Robey, Foden and Sentinel produced machines of considerable sophistication. The Foden D-type was fitted with a special three-way valve which enabled the driver to exercise much greater control over the passage of steam to the cylinders, and roller bearings were added to the motion for smooth operation. Sentinel made an undermounted tractor which gave excellent

vision to the driver, and had a vertical boiler with a chute to feed the firebox.

The sad thing, as far as British manufacturers were concerned, was that they had been forced to wait so long before it was worth their while to consider new ideas, let alone put them into practice. Elsewhere new ideas had already been developed. Many steam tractors were no more than smaller versions of the familiar traction engine. The French, however, began to look at new ways of improving performance in light engines. Léon Serpollet, inventor of the steam tricycle, solved one problem – how to generate steam rapidly and at high pressure. His flash boiler first appeared in 1889. Water was pumped to the bottom of a series of red hot, nickel-steel coiled tubes. It was converted almost instantly into steam and as it passed up the system, so it became superheated and its expansive force considerably increased. It brought the age of the light vehicle a lot nearer. The Serpollet boiler became popular for steam tractors, hauling both passengers and freight. De Dion also began manufacturing steam tractors, but he very soon turned to another new idea. The next stage was to join the load-carrying trailer to the engine to create a single unit. The result was the steam wagon. Hundreds of de Dion wagons were produced, but in 1900 he turned away from steam altogether, to become one of the foremost pioneers

BELOW: This American, general-purpose engine photographed in the 1890s is hauling a thresher of the period, which is typical of those seen during the late nineteenth century.

of the internal combustion engine. Soon there was only one steam wagon manufacturer left in France, Purrey, who remained in business from 1898 to 1929.

America joined the fray in the early 1900s and by 1902 the Michigan Steam Motor Company had been established in Detroit. They built some astonishing machines. These were fired using light oils and the boilers were placed directly beneath the driver's seat, and with working pressures of 350psi (24 bar) one can only assume that the drivers had complete confidence in their manufacturers. The engine was a complex affair, with two sets of cylinders arranged in V-formation, one high pressure, two intermediaries and a low pressure, to each side of the V. It was all a bit too complicated and rather ahead of its time, for good trunk roads were not really common in America until after World War I. Detroit had by that time abandoned steam and was set on the path that was to lead it to become the biggest centre for motor car, or automobile, manufacture in the world.

Once British manufacturers got the legal go-ahead, they were to prove enthusiastic developers of the steam wagon, and some at least were not even prepared to wait for changes in the law before they got started. James Sumner of Leyland in Lancashire built a 5-ton wagon in 1894. It worked perfectly well, but the customers, Stanning's Bleach Works, bowed to local opposition and the wagon made just one journey, managing to collect a fine along the way. In 1892, Sumner inherited his father's engineering works, which was in a far from healthy financial state. He was not prepared to take further risks by developing more steam wagons, but he did produce a highly profitable line of steam lawn mowers. This put the firm back into

LEFT: Crane engines are rare, but they are welcome visitors to any steam fair. This rather cumbersome-looking Ransome was to be seen at Newbury in 1991.

BELOW: This formidable Aveling and Porter of 1879, featuring a simple jib crane that is controlled from the driving position, has been pressed into military service and is seen here in action as it easily lifts a gun from its limber.

ABOVE: This venerable traction engine was put to work delivering laundry in Sunderland in 1957, during the Suez War crisis, when there was no petrol but plenty of coal.

RIGHT: Aveling and Porter's catalogue showed the various ways their basic steam wagons could be used. This adaptation of a 5-ton wagon as an open truck was built in 1919.

profit and left him in a position to take advantage of the relaxations in the law. With new partners, George and Henry Spurrier, who had experience with railway locomotive design, the Lancashire Steam Motor Company was founded. A 1.5-ton van was soon followed by a 3-ton truck and the Leyland works were well on their way. The first vehicles were oil-fired, but they soon reverted to coal and by 1902 they had expanded to a new factory. Lancashire, inevitably, had rivals across the Pennines in the shape of the Yorkshire Patent Steam Wagon Company. Their wagons were unique, with the boiler mounted transversely in front of the driver, an economical way of arranging engine components that appeared half a century before the more famous Mini.

NEW COMPETITION

The development of the steam wagon coincided with that of the diesel engine. Because we know the outcome of the struggle we tend to think of the steam engine as being fated from the start and only feel surprised that it remained in use as long as it did. Certainly, many manufacturers, even if they were not prepared to make a complete change to the internal combustion engine, were prepared to hedge their bets. Leyland were offering customers a choice as early as 1904. In fact, their research had indicated that there was a place for both. The petrol and diesel engine won out for low loads up to 4 tons. Up to 6 tons there was little to choose between them, but beyond this steam was definitely to be preferred. Another major factor that came into

the equation was that, being based on a new technology, the first motor trucks were far from reliable. On the famous Emancipation Run from London to Brighton in 1896, which marked the end of the red flag days and which is still rerun every year with vintage and veteran cars, the breakdown van carrying spares and equipment itself broke down more often than the cars it was supposed to be serving.

Even if there was an inevitability about the final outcome, the steam men fought to the last. The story of the steam car does not fall within the remit of this book, but as an example of just what could be achieved it is perhaps worth mentioning the

incredible American steam sports car, the Doble, first built in 1924. With a flash boiler that could produce steam at 750psi (51 bar) in just over half a minute, it could accelerate from 0 to 40mph (64km/h) in eight seconds and had a top speed of over 100mph (160km/h). Sadly it was also incredibly expensive, and in seven years only 45 models were sold, one of them being bought by the famous American inventor and entrepreneur Howard Hughes. In the end, the future of steam was largely determined by economics, especially in Britain, where once again the government was cast in the role of villain. The 1933 Road Traffic Act trebled the licence fee for steam vehicles, while

at the same time reducing it on diesels. It marked the end of steam development on the roads of Britain, but perhaps not everyone mourned its passing.

The life of the men who worked with the great engines was unremittingly hard. Out in all weathers and all seasons in unprotected cabs, working long hours of hard physical labour, and with nothing much to look forward to at the end of the day but the minimum comforts of the living van, it was not an enviable life. Nor was it a life without its dangers. To the general public, the great danger appeared to be boiler explosions. They did occur, generally as a result of negligence or corner cutting. It was

not unknown for unscrupulous owners to try to make up time by tampering with safety valves. Again a fusible plug, an essential safeguard against overheating and running dry, was often replaced on a 'temporary' basis by a far from fusible alternative, rather than lose time waiting for a replacement to arrive. Boiler water could be allowed to run dry simply because the driver had been quenching his own thirst. All these factors could contribute to a disaster which could mean not just the loss of an engine but more importantly a loss of life. But if the boiler explosion was by far the most spectacular accident that could overtake an engine, it was not the most common. All kinds of things could cause an engine to come to grief. It could slide off into a ditch or fall through a weak bridge – on one occasion a cellar below a busy road gave way and down the engine went. Running out of control down a hill was dangerous not only for the men on the engine but for everyone in its path as well. One hapless lady of Strood on the Medway in southeast England was woken early one morning in 1908 by a crash of bricks, timber and plaster to find an Aveling and Porter engine in the middle of her front room. Amazingly no one was harmed.

Yet, on the whole, the accidents were no worse than those on modern roads, and a good deal fewer. The engines did a valuable job and did it well, and if not everyone came to love the panting monsters, at least there was one time when they were always welcome: when they brought the fair to town. And that is a subject that deserves a section all to itself.

LEFT: A Yorkshire Steam Wagon Company vehicle at a rally, with its neat transverse engine. Behind it can be seen a very handsome showman's living wagon.

BELOW: Part of the enduring appeal of the traction engine lies in the careful attention to detail, gleaming paint, attractive designs and shining brass.

CHAPTER 4

ALL THE FUN OF THE FAIR

Fairs have been with us since Roman times, and for a very long time they existed to carry out serious business. There were horse fairs where livestock was traded and hiring fairs where farm labourers and others traded in their own labour, putting themselves out to hire. At the same time, they had always had a lighter side, and the name itself comes down from the Latin *feria*, to the Old French *feire*, meaning 'holiday'. It was natural that such occasions should attract all kinds

attraction began to appear: the rides. These started with simple swing boats, where the paying customers did the work themselves, and simple hand-operated carousels or round-abouts. The fairground, or tober as the showmen themselves called it, was becoming more important than the old working fair itself. It was run by showmen and their families, always on the move, spending their lives in horse-drawn caravans or 'living wagons' as the showmen themselves pre-

of people anxious to make what they could out of the massed crowds, and these included entertainers of all kinds. In time, the serious side of the business faded away – girls no longer carried mops to mop fairs to show they were available for domestic service, and there were very few geese for sale at the goose fair – but the name lived on and the fairs lived on with their travelling shows and showmen.

As the years went by, new elements were added. Menageries were popular for a time, and all kinds of sideshows offered customers ways of losing their money. Then a different kind of

ferred to call them, and hauling the rides and sideshows along on carts. No one can be certain who first had the notion of applying the traction engine to this job, but the honour is generally awarded to an American circus owner, Jim Myers, who came to England and paraded into Folkestone on 13 August 1859, the procession led by a single Bray engine. The engine could hardly have done very much work, but to many in the town it would have seemed every bit as exotic as the lion tamer and his lions. It was a start, but not one which had any immediate effect. Circus owners remained reluctant to turn to steam for haulage, fearing that the noise and smoke would disturb the animals. It is equally doubtful if many showmen at that time would have seen much advantage in exchanging their tried and trusted horses for a new, complicated machine, even if they could have afforded one. When change came, it arrived because the nature of the fair itself was beginning to change.

The first change came courtesy of a very different group of

ABOVE: An old postcard shows the crowds at Nottingham Goose Fair, England, in the 1900s, with puffs of smoke rising from the various steam engines that are working the rides and lighting the fairground.
LEFT: The gaudy splendour of this rank of steam gallopers recall the glory days of fairgrounds before the World War I. The central organ can be just seen.

ABOVE: A splendid set of steam gallopers, with smoke emerging from the central engine that provided the power for what was an exciting and popular ride.

RIGHT: The showmen adapted the traction engine to their own purposes. Like the rides, it was brightly coloured with a canopy carried on twisted pillars. This is an 1876 Burrell.

people, the scientists. As early as 1800 the Italian physicist Alessandro Volta (1745–1827) had shown that electricity could be generated by immersing metal plates in a suitable solution. It was originally known as a 'voltaic pile' and then later a 'voltaic battery', finally arriving at the name we have today, just plain battery. The inventor's name was not lost, however, surviving in the familiar electrical unit, the volt. It took no more than a couple of years to discover that if carbon electrodes were added to the battery, a brilliant arc could pass between them. It took about forty years for that observation to be translated into a practical device, the arc lamp. It was the first efficient form of electric light, but it still required a vast array of heavy batteries to make it work. The results, however, spurred on others. Joseph Swan in Britain and Thomas Edison in America came up with the much more useful filament light bulb. In 1882 they joined forces to create the Edison and Swan United Electric Light Company, and electric lighting began to develop along the lines that we now know today. The efficient light bulb had arrived, but what was still needed was a better method of supplying it with power. This is not a science text book, but the following is a brief summary of what the scientists were up to in the years while electric lighting was being produced.

NEW TECHNOLOGY

The French physicist and mathematician André Ampère (1775–1836) – who was to join Volta in providing names for units – discovered the connection between electricity and magnetism. The idea was promptly seized by the English physicist and chemist Michael Faraday (1791–1867), who boldly wrote in his notebook one day that he had a new objective in life, to 'convert magnetism into electricity'. By 1831 he had succeeded, and promptly lost interest. As far as he was concerned, the problem had been solved and others could do what they liked with the result. Many did. The principle was simple enough: if you move an armature in the field of an electro-magnet you will produce an electric current. The device became known as a

dynamo-electric generator, or just plain dynamo. There were to be many steps along the path to providing an efficient generator, but one problem was an ancient and familiar one. The dynamo had to go round. On a large scale, water power could be used and the water turbine producing hydro-electricity is still with us today. But anything that could be turned by water could just as easily be turned by steam.

By the 1880s, efficient electric lighting was well and truly on its way, and how the showmen longed to have a part of it. What they needed, however, was something small-scale and portable. That became a possibility when John Hopkinson, who was a consultant engineer with Edison, invented the light, carbon-brush dynamo.

Anyone who has ever visited a fair knows that while it can be fun by day, it is twice as alluring by night. Lamps sparkle above the gaudy rides, booths are beckoning, beacons shining out through the darkness. It needed a certain amount of imagination, however, to see how the rather dull, plodding traction engine might have a part in this glittering story. It was fine down on the farm or heaving itself along, dragging a heavy load, but it was hardly thought of as an angel of light. One man who did see the possibilities was a gentleman who has already appeared in the story as a dashing and inventive individual, R.E.B. Crompton, of the Indian road train (see Chapter 3). In 1879, he devised a dynamo that could be driven, as many other machines were already being driven, by means of a belt wrapped round the flywheel of a steam engine. He worked with Marshalls of Gainsborough and that summer the device was given a highly successful trial run, lighting the partying and junketing at the Henley Regatta. So it was that in the 1880s, the combination of the electric light bulb and the small, portable generator, promised a new, exciting world for the showmen.

THE 'ELECTRIC LIGHT ENGINES'

Once a thing has been shown to be possible then, provided that enough people need it, development soon begins to quicken its pace. The first attempts at lighting showgrounds and fairs were rather tentative. A portable steam engine was wheeled onto the site and hitched up to a separate dynamo. Improvements were soon made, when two companies, Thomas Green of Leeds and Savage of King's Lynn produced what they described as 'electric light engines' specifically designed for showmen. These had the engine and dynamo mounted together on the same chassis, so it was no longer necessary to manoeuvre separate elements around in order to get everything correctly in line and set them the right distance apart. But, in a way, this was a step back to the first years of agricultural engines, when teams of horses pulled a machine that could have been made to drive itself. This state of affairs had been a source of irritation to Thomas Aveling years before, so it is no surprise to find Aveling and Porter being among the first to tackle the current problem. They built a dynamo above the motion of a traction engine, where it could be driven through gearing. It was Burrells, however, who came up with a far simpler idea. They mounted the dynamo on a bracket set in front of the chimney, and now it could be worked as the earlier versions had been by a simple belt drive from the flywheel. And that was that. Nobody really tried to find a better arrangement, and the showman's engine had arrived.

BELOW: One of the main jobs of the showman's engine was to generate electricity for lighting. The familiar gallopers are thus transformed by night.

Just how many old engines were adapted to the new system is simply not known, but we do know the very first engine to be built from scratch, complete with dynamo, and delivered to a showman, was Burrell No. 1451 built in 1889 for Jacob Studt of Pontypridd, and given a suitably imposing name – *Monarch*. Jacob Studt's Steam Circus was sufficiently impressive to feature in Burrell's catalogue for 1909. But what was his circus, and how was steam to be used? The answer to those questions brings us on to the next part of the story, away from changes in laboratory and factory and back to the fairground, where Studt will soon put in another appearance.

LIFE ON THE MOVE

In the early days of sideshows, many a fairground traveller could move from site to site with all his possessions in a barrow, if it was, for example, nothing more complex than a hoopla stall or coconut shy, and anything just a little grander could be strapped to the back of a pack horse. Only the grandest rose to the exalted heights of a horse-drawn cart or van. All that began to change with the development of the rides. Some of the earliest were primitive forms of roundabouts, where a circle of planks was suspended from a central pole. Wooden horses or other animals were mounted on the planks and the whole thing set in motion by the simple expedient of pushing it round. The length of the ride depended on the good temper and strength of the man supplying the muscle power. A photograph from about 1860 shows Twigdon's Riding Machine, with a man in the middle to whom such a task would have been assigned, wearing a rather dashing stovepipe hat, making him look quite like the famous English engineer Isambard Brunel. A rather more sophisticated version with a crank and gears was built as early as the 1830s but was perhaps a bit too expensive for this Brunel look-alike. And this, of course, was the problem for engine salesmen. As long as this was literally the biggest attraction on the fairground, there was not going to be either a demand for steam power nor the money to pay for it.

The successful showman was, however, a great user of horse power. His caravan was his home, and a very well-appointed home it was in many cases, with a wealth of plush and cut glass that would have graced any Victorian parlour. A man who had developed more than one attraction would have needed both a string of horses and men to look after them. The expense was considerable, for this was strictly a summer activity and once the season had ended, the income ceased but not the costs. The animals still needed to be looked after, fed and provided with winter quarters. Just such a dilemma faced other users of road transport. The alternative – making greater use of the railways – was not really feasible at least in Britain, where the gauge greatly limited the size of load that could be carried. In other countries,

notably France, showmen did use specially designed vehicles, longer and lower to allow them to be moved on trains.

The idea of using traction engines for the straightforward task of haulage was developed only slowly, and when steam was used the showmen generally preferred to hire engines and their crew as needed. But the need for a better form of transport was growing steadily throughout the latter part of the nineteenth century. It came with what was really the next obvious step in the development of rides. As the rides got bigger, manpower could give way to animal power and that was bound in the long term to be replaced by steam power.

Probably the first adaptation was the transformation of the old 'dobbies', as rides with wooden horses were known, into the altogether more dashing Steam Gallopers. They seem to have been converted to steam for the very first time in 1865, when showman S.G. Soames caused a sensation at Aylesham Fair in Norfolk with the new wonder. One of the earliest manufacturers to build special steam rides, as opposed to adapting old ones, was Savage, who started with what were called Platform Rides. The horses were mounted on the rotating platform, and a wheel under each horse turned as the platform turned, so that the horses bobbed up and down. More sophisticated gallopers soon appeared which had the horses suspended by poles from a rotating top. Here the galloping action was produced by bevel gearing from the central drive activating cranks attached to the horse supports. As rides got faster the poles were passed through slots in the lower platform, so that as they gathered speed, the horse could move outward under centrifugal force. This was not intended to add excitement to the ride, but to reduce it, as otherwise there was a real danger that the rider would be forced out, minus the horse.

FAIRGROUND ATTRACTION

The new rides were expensive and they needed to advertise their presence to draw in the paying customers. Colours were brilliant, with gilt lavishly applied. An extra attraction was often supplied by a steam organ. In some cases this stood by the engine at the centre of the ride, or it could be separated and made into a grand feature in its own right. The fairground organ developed as a natural successor to the barrel organ, which had been known at fairs for many years. In the old instrument, a barrel studded with pins was turned by a handle. The studs depressed keys attached to the organ pipes to produce the notes, and different arrangements of pins on the barrel produced different tunes. The fairground organ was developed by European manufacturers such as Gavioli in the 1870s and was altogether grander. Instead of studs on a barrel, the control was through 'the book', a card folded concertina wise and punched with holes. Its workings were the opposite of those of the barrel

organ. When the card was first fed into the organ it depressed all the keys to the pipes, which could only rise again where a hole appeared as the card was moved steadily along. The new organs did not just produce simple tunes with limited harmonic and tonal range, they could play complex chords, reproduce the sounds of different instruments, bang drums and clash cymbals. The grandest of machines, such as the Gavioli Orchestraphones, had a total of 110 keys and were sumptuous in appearance. Their fronts displayed a baroque exuberance of curlicues and scrolls, while an animated figure would dance to the music or conduct the mechanical orchestra. Happily, these splendid instruments

still survive, and it is a skilled but still feasible task to create brand new books.

The big organs often had their own portable steam engines to drive the mechanism. They would be set down next to the biggest and grandest rides, and the rides were getting bigger and grander all the time. A natural development from the gallopers was the chairoplane, an idea first developed in Germany. Instead of poles holding horses or other beasts, chairs were suspended by chains from the rotating top. It worked like a giant centrifuge with the riders, usually screaming at the tops of their voices, flying out over the heads of the crowd. The showmen

ABOVE: By the 1920s, the old rides had lost their attraction and new entertainments for the Jazz Age came in. The Cakewalk, with its shaking floor, was very popular.

LEFT: The showman's engine was always a very versatile machine that found many uses around the fairground, here providing power for a small steam organ.

were always on the look out for such novelties. As the nineteenth century came to an end, so the formal dances of the Victorian age gave way to more frenetic new dances from America, that developed with the arrival of ragtime and the birth of jazz. The Cakewalk took its name from one of the dances made popular in the touring minstrel shows. The ride consisted of a series of shaking platforms, moved backwards and forwards and up and down by a simple system of cranks. The challenge was to walk along it or, if you were very confident, try and dance without falling over. The more that you fell over the more the crowds gathered to laugh and egged their friends on to have a go. Steam

was also applied to other traditional amusements, such as swings which could be made to swoop up and down in a most satisfactory stomach-churning manner. Looming over them all was what was literally the biggest of all fairground attractions, the Ferris wheel.

SPIRIT OF ENTERPRISE

Something very new began to appear at fairs at the very end of the nineteenth century: the Bioscope, forerunner of the modern cinema. It was the trade name of a company set up by an American, Charles Urban, to supply all the necessary equipment for shooting films and projecting them. He was a good deal more than just a manufacturer, he was also a man of bold ideas and one of the first to see the possibilities of what we now call newsreels. He sent off his own reporter together with his bulky equipment to film the Boer War, and even though the cameraman never managed to get very close to the action, the films created huge interest. There were no purpose-built cinemas, so the Bioscopes took to the road, first appearing at fairgrounds in 1896. Among the pioneers who toured Bioscopes was Jacob Studt, whom we last met buying his new Burrell in 1889 for his steam circus. We actually know what the Studt Bioscope looked like from photographs. It was a tremendously grand affair, with a heavily ornamented facade lit by arc lamps. A magnificent organ stood by the entrance and even the steam engine, not the original Burrell but a later purchase, was heavily ornamented to blend in with the facade. Behind this immense frontage was a simple marquee able to hold a thousand spectators. If anything could be said to typify the gaudy grandeur, elaboration and splendour of the fair it was the Bioscope. Now, with the demand for electric lighting almost universal, with rides and entertainments getting bigger all the

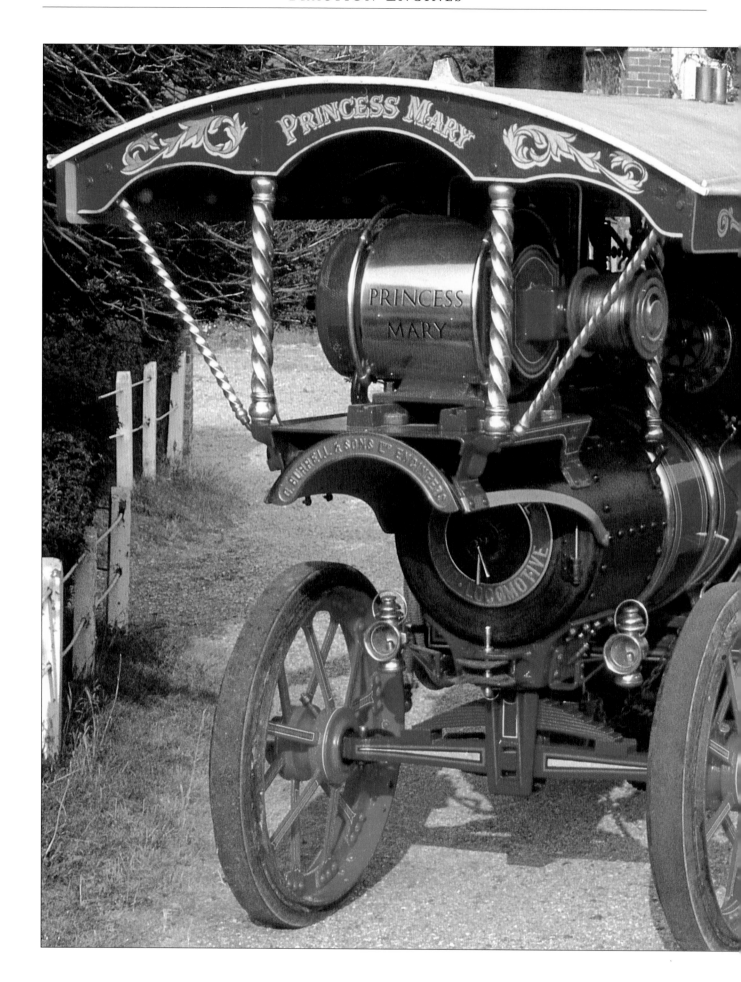

time, the replacement of the horse by the traction engine was all but inevitable.

It is easy now to see the enormous advantages offered by steam traction, but then we have very little concept of what life on the fairground was like in the days of the horse and we also tend not to think of the showmen as being big business men but just itinerant entertainers. But a showman with a full range of sideshows and rides was in charge of a considerable enterprise and owner of a good deal of valuable property. He differed from other property owners, however, in that his was always on the move. Frances Brown, descendent of a very well-known travelling family in Britain, the Matthews, told the story of several generations in her book *Fairfield Folk* (Malvern Publishing, 1986). William 'Redshirt' Matthews, who was born in 1843, was typical of many others in that he was totally illiterate, yet ran a considerable business on his own. Before the start of each season, he would do the round of traditional sites to book his dates, signing each contract with a cross. At the end of his rounds he had a whole year's itinerary in his head and refused to divulge it to anyone, not even to his own family. When the fair was pulled down at one location, he would ride off in a pony and trap and leave a trail for the rest to follow – for even at that late date they were not to be let into the secret. When he bought his first steam galloper he was still entirely dependent on horses for transport, and moving the new ride around was quite a business. The centre truck, the wheeled platform with the engine permanently fixed in the middle, needed four horses to pull it. The ride itself had to be broken down into separate loads, each of which needed three horses, and the assembly was completed by the living wagon which needed another pair of horses. In order to ensure that he always had enough horses available for work, he had to keep around a hundred of them. In 1883, he took the big decision and went off to Savage who supplied him with two engines, duly recorded in the works' order book. No.282 was a simple vertical organ engine, but the workhorse was No. 285 a two-cylinder traction engine, designed to pull a 34-ft (10-m) diameter roundabout with 24 horses, mounted two abreast. This was a big investment but it soon paid its way. He was to order more engines as the years went by.

The story of steam haulage by showmen was not always one of total success. On a memorable day in September 1913 the Matthews were on the move. The procession was making its way down the slope of the Chilterns towards High Wycombe. The centre truck and gallopers were on three trailers hauled by a single-cylinder Savage. In front was the living wagon, pulled by

LEFT: This photograph of a Burrell, described as the 'Pride of Dorset', provides a very good view of the front-mounted dynamo, powered by the engine to produce electricity.

ABOVE: The Fowler engine, *Renown*, having hauled a ride to the fairground, has now erected a jib at the back to start the work of building it up so that it is ready to operate as a crowd-pulling attraction.

another engine. Because of the steepness of the descent it was prudent to change to a lower gear. It was even more prudent to stop the engine before doing so and all the manuals stressed how dangerous it was to change on the move. But the Savage crew decided to attempt to save time by trying it anyway – and failed. Now the engine was free wheeling out of control, forced on by the huge weight behind it, heading towards the wagon in front. To avoid a double catastrophe, the steerer turned his Fowler in towards the bank at the side of the road. It hit with a huge crash, somersaulted and ended on its back. The confusion was immense, painted animals and birds from the ride were strewn across the road; the engine, its motion shattered, was enveloped in steam. A man called Thomas Ryan dashed in through the hissing clouds to pull out the injured men. The driver and steerer recovered, but the damage to engine and ride was immense, and the other showmen contributed to a fund to help out 'Redshirt' Matthews. The donations give an indication of the range of resources that might be found on any fairground. At the top of the list was W. Wilson, owner of the big switchback who gave over thirteen pounds, while small stall holders did what they could, which in some cases meant a donation of just half a crown (22 pence).

Happily, such accidents were as rare among fairground travellers as they were in other forms of steam road haulage, and on the whole the showmen had every reason to be grateful for their mechanical aids. There was, apart from the dynamo, no real difference between showmen's engines and any other road locomotive. The same manufacturers' names regularly appear. Burrells were pre-eminent, first providing single-cylinder and later compound engines, mainly double-cranked. Fowlers of Leeds and Foster of Lincoln were equally well known, while Savages of King's Lynn were notable as builders of rides as well as engines. Any traction engine could be pressed into service for the straightforward work of haulage. In the 1920s one British showman, Sam Brumby, created something of a stir by using a Kemna traction engine, manufactured in Germany. But if the engines were unremarkable mechanically, they certainly did not look in the least like other road locomotives.

THE SHOWMAN'S ENGINE

The first thing that is inevitably striking in a showman's engine is the decoration. It may be quite restrained – at least when seen in terms of fairground decoration as a whole – or it can be wildly exotic. It is obvious why this should be so. On its long journeys through the countryside, the ride itself is no more than a series of nondescript objects wrapped in waterproof sheeting. There may be a name on the side, but why should anyone be bothered to look at it? If anyone is going to take notice, then it has to be the engine itself that demands attention. Sleek, glossy paintwork, usually in a rich maroon, provides the background colour, which is then decorated with coloured stars and roundels. Wheels are brightly painted in either yellow or maroon, often said quite erroneously to show whether the owner was of Romany or Irish descent. There was a very real chance that he was neither, and nothing more enraged a proud showman than to have his elegant and often very beautiful living wagon referred to as a 'gypsy caravan'. However, to return to the engine, the most obvious distinguishing feature, apart from the dynamo at the front, is the canopy. This stretches the full length of the machine, with a hole for the chimney, and is supported on twisted, 'barley sugar' pillars, always kept gleaming bright. Along the top of the canopy, in beautiful lettering, will be found the name of the owner and the ride. There may have been exceptions to this general pattern, but the only anomaly that seems to have been photographed was the Studt Bioscope engine, mentioned earlier, where the canopy was moulded to match the extravagant decoration of the show's facade. The general pattern is the one that survives in all pre-

served engines. It is no wonder that the survivors are so popular with the fair-going public, but sadly they rarely get the opportunity to see the engines doing the full range of jobs for which they were designed. As one of those who has been privileged to watch a whole set-up, what follows is a description of just one build-up that took place on a sunny afternoon just before the opening of the Great Dorset Steam Fair.

THE STORY OF RENOWN

The engine in this case was a Fowler, *Renown*, every inch a showman's engine, but for one curious anomaly. It is painted blue. The name of the original owner is emblazoned across the canopy – John Murphy's Proud Peacocks. Now it seems that when Mr Murphy ordered his new engine, he had reasonably expected it to be ready in time for the start of the new season, but for some reason Fowlers were delayed and when Murphy arrived at the works it was still in its blue undercoat. He and the peacocks, however, could wait no longer, so off it went unfinished. It was supposed to be returned for the conventional finish to be applied at the end of the season, but by then Murphy

BELOW: One of the most famous of old fairground attractions, Harry Lee's hundred-year-old swing boats. Early visitors to showgrounds may well see *Renown* erecting them.

ABOVE: Nothing on a fairground is ever drab, and that includes the working engines. The colours are always bright, with stars and roundels as traditional decoration.

RIGHT: The showman's engine not only provided power to light and run the rides, they too were brightly lit at night. Bulbs surround the canopy of this Garrett 33486.

had grown to like the colour he had, so blue it remained. And it has to be said that the deep royal blue presents a very handsome effect.

Renown, however, was not on this occasion required for Proud Peacocks or any other roundabout, but was to play a role in erecting a splendid and venerable fairground ride, Harry Lee's Steam Yachts. The name was originally given in an attempt to capitalise on the huge interest roused by Sir Thomas Lipton's many attempts between 1899 and 1914 to win the prestigious yachting trophy, the America's Cup, for Britain. Harry Lee's Steam Yachts may not have been the streamlined giants of ocean racing, but at least the two great swing boats were evenly matched, one with the Union Jack on the bottom, the other with the Stars and Stripes. The first part of the job was, as always, transportation. As with the centre truck of the gallopers, the yachts have a permanently mounted centre engine to supply the power, making up one entire load, the rest being hauled in on flat trucks.

Once on the site, *Renown* had to go through a minor transformation. A simple jib crane forms a standard part of the engine's equipment. The jib and its guides have to be taken down and fixed in place by a simple pinion to a bracket at the rear of the engine. The showman's engine had now become a crane engine. A basic frame was laid out on the ground, after which timber A-frames that were to form the main support for the swing boats were raised by the jib and located in sockets on the base. With the frame complete, the drive engine could be wheeled into place, the two big swing boats suspended and fixed to the chain

drive. A simple clutch mechanism allows the two swing boats to be worked independently. This is not quite all, for what would such a splendid ride be without music? A small Chiappa Organ, presided over by the figure of Johann Strauss, complete with its own small steam donkey engine was added, and now the assembly was complete. All that remained was to get up steam and the fun could begin. *Renown's* jib was now removed and the engine manoeuvred into place for its next task. An extension chimney was added to keep the clouds of smoke clear of the crowds, and

the electric cables could be connected up to the dynamo. The ride could now be lit and shown in all its splendour and *Renown* too benefited as night fell and lights came on all round the canopy.

Harry Lee's Steam Yachts required three separate engines to make everything work, and this was true of other rides as well. Some manufacturers thought that was at least one too many. It seemed logical to devise some means by which the haulage engine itself could be used as the power source for the ride. The simplest form involved extending the hornplates that rose from the firebox, an arrangement first introduced on steam rollers (see Chapter 5), so that a turret could be built up above the motion. This was quite a large structure which had to rise high enough to carry the cheese wheel, the rotary wheel of the galloper. The drive was either supplied by a vertical shaft from the crankshaft, or by a second, small engine mounted on the turret. Once the base of the ride was securely in place, the traction engine was then driven up onto the central truck, which needed

RIGHT: There is no more exciting sight at a steam fair than that of a phalanx of showmen's engines all lined up and illuminated in preparation for the night's fun.

to be a very substantial affair to take the weight. The advantages were clear, and the ride master could control everything from a central position, but there were disadvantages as well. Once the traction engine was in place, it was certainly ready to power the ride, but the ride itself had still to be completed. The jib crane could no longer be used, trucks could not be manoeuvred, so everything had to be done by hand. It all made for very hard work, but some at least thought the benefits outweighed the problems.

NEW DEVELOPMENTS

The ingenuity shown by different manufacturers in getting one engine to do a variety of jobs was remarkable. Savages were first into the fray with a patent in 1880 and suggestions for different arrangements, one of which included an organ actually fastened to the front of the engine. It might have been a great success on a permanent site, but it would have been a nightmare on the move. Like many patents, it was intended to establish a practice and close out any opposition, rather than as a blueprint for an actual working engine. Savages went on to build a number of engines using the turret principle. Fowlers built an engine similar to the Savage, called the Whirligig Engine, which took its drive from the main engine, but used a smaller engine mounted on the side of the smoke box to work an organ. At least the Whirligig could be moved down the road in safety. Burrell took out his patent in 1895 for what was the most sophisticated of all the versions. There were two overhead cylinders to produce the drive for the cheese wheel, taking their steam from the main boiler, while the engine itself was still available to operate the dynamo for lighting. That represented a great deal of steam power and would have kept the driver very busy indeed maintaining pressure. In the event, what with the complexities of these arrangements and the problems that arose when it came to building up and pulling down, the all-purpose engines had a limited appeal.

New developments in rides made new demands on the engines. Savages, as always, were among the innovators and one of their most important novelties, introduced in 1880, was a device variously known as a switchback or scenic railway. In the early version it was no more than a variation on the steam galloper, except that carriages were substituted for horses and they were made to run round on an undulating track. In time, these were converted to electric power, providing a much heavier work load for the showman's engine and its dynamo. The first electrically powered scenic railway appeared in 1910, but there were

problems still to overcome. The scenic railway generally had eight passenger cars, and getting these started from rest called for a heavy surge of current, which the usual dynamo was not always able to supply. So a separate device was added, known as the exciter, which was driven by a belt from the main dynamo. The exciter was not used often, for once the ride had started it was seldom allowed to stop, just slowed down to a very slow crawl for passengers to get on and off. Now specialist scenic engines were developed. They were supplied with rear mounted crane, dynamo and exciter, and an extra wide flywheel to accommodate

a 9-in (23-cm) drive built compared with the normal 7-in (18-cm) used with the standard dynamo. A Burrell 8-hp engine could produce 29,700 watts for the main dynamo and an extra 8,800 watts for the exciter. Even this was not always enough as the rides got bigger and even more exotic. One especially grand scenic railway required two engines – one to do the hard work, the other to supply the glamour. This ride not only had the usual mighty organ and a profusion of lights, but also featured an illuminated cascade, a waterfall that needed water to be constantly pumped and recirculated. To keep all this lot on the go, the

engines had to work flat out with steam often reaching the maximum pressure of 200psi (13.6 bar).

This was hard work for the engine men, who had to keep their charges going nonstop, from whatever time in the morning they first got up steam until late at night when the fair closed down. It was a never-ending round of firing up, oiling round, boiler filling and dealing with any problems that might arise, all without ever allowing the engine to stop. Clearing out tubes and fireboxes were daily chores, which meant that there was little time for routine maintenance. It is to the credit of both engine

men and manufacturers that the engines stood up to the harsh treatment, so that many have survived to please us today.

All showmen were publicity conscious, and eager to grasp at any device that would attract paying customers. G.T. Tuby, for example, had a particularly fine scenic, known as Tuby's Circular Railway. It was rich with carving, liberally splashed with gilt and the gondolas waltzed round to the sound of its organ. During the Boer War (1899–1902), when patriotic fervour was running high, pictures of British generals adorned the toppers, the carved and decorated panels attached to the rounding board, the main board at the top of the ride. Then, as memories of the war faded, a new attraction caught the public imagination – the motor car. Out went the whiskered generals and the gondolas, and a new name was painted on the rounding board – Tuby and Sons 60hp Panhard Motors. Tuby himself was a Doncaster man,

LEFT: This Fowler's proud message is no idle boast. The engines had to do immense work, moving between sites, then running through the day and into the night.
BELOW: The appeal of the showman's engine is obvious. This splendid Burrell has been magnificently restored, right down to the vintage carriage lamps.

who became involved in local politics. In popular mythology, showmen were travellers, forever on the move, but men such as Tuby had considerable capital tied up in their enterprise and operated from a permanent home base. Anyway, Tuby was duly elected to Doncaster council, and when he acquired a new Burrell engine it was called *Councillor*. Subsequent engines reflected his rise up the local government ladder: *Councillor* was followed by *Alderman* and his arrival at the pinnacle was celebrated when *Mayor* appeared. This was not quite the end of the line of engine names, for Tuby was clearly a man with little pomposity and considerable good humour, and the last engine in the series was duly titled *Ex-Mayor*. Another engine that was something of a private joke around the fairs was *The Russell Baby*, a reference to the philandering owner's involvement with a well-publicised paternity case.

Names were sometimes amusing, but they were more likely to be grandiose – *Marvel, Marvellous, Samson* and the like. The engines were not always as grand as their name might suggest. *Ex-Mayor* was, in fact, Burrell No.4000 built in 1925, and when the Tubys sold her on just six years later she was in a very poor condition. The boiler had not been washed out for weeks, the firebox was in a deplorable state, many of the boiler tubes had holes and

steam whistled out of the glands. Yet the old engine was quickly restored by her new owner Frank Cheffins, and a photograph of 1934 shows her in prime condition, everything sparkling as new. Perhaps too much blame should not be attached to the owners and drivers. The old maxim 'the show must go on' was as applicable to the fair as it was to the theatre, and as well as the heavy, unremitting work of the fairground itself, there were the long drives in between, which provided just as much hard labour for the long-suffering engine – and just as little spare time for maintenance.

LEGISLATION

In the early days, regulations allowed a single engine to tow up to nine vehicles at a time. It seems impossible for such very long trains to be managed by a single engine, but in 1895 William Murphy wrote to Fowlers congratulating them on the power of the new engine he had just purchased, which had worked perfectly well with a ten-vehicle tow! Just how this could have been achieved with any degree of safety is difficult to imagine, since the driver at the front could have had only the vaguest idea of what was going on at the rear of his road train. The law was changed in 1896 and the number was reduced to three vehicles plus water cart. Even so, it made for a heavy and unwieldy train. For most of the period when they were in regular use, the engines had steel wheels, but the following carts and wagons had plain wooden wheels, of the kind used on generations of farm carts and horse wagons, with metal tyres and brass-bushed hubs. Overheating was common on long journeys, and it was by no means unusual for a wheel to catch fire on the move. As with all heavy loads steep hills were the real problem. For very stiff climbs, it was often necessary to have to break the load and make two separate journeys. It was going downhill that presented the great danger. Even if the driver did all the right things, stopping to engage low gear before starting the descent, the weight of the load might be too great for the engine, which would begin an inexorable acceleration. In the more sophisticated trains involving the big loads, trucks were individually braked and there was a system of communication between the men on the loads and the driver, either by bell or steam whistle. This was very far from being true of all trains, however. Some engines had to pull unbraked trucks. In these cases, the only means of slowing them was to jump off and push wooden wedges in front of the wheels so that they slid instead of turning. If that failed a pole would be taken off the load and shoved through the spokes into the springing to hold it firm. Even if the

RIGHT: Today the engines themselves are the main attractions at steam fairs, so that an ordinary road engine is not out of place among the glamorous showmen's engines.

pole snapped, at least the truck would have been slowed. This alarming task was often entrusted to quite young members of the family, in spite of its all too obvious dangers. But whether wholly up-to-date or crudely unsophisticated, big loads were never easy to manage. It is not unreasonable to say that no engine in the steam age was made to work harder for its living than the showman's engine.

The big road locomotives were not the only engines used by showmen. The change in the law that allowed tractors under 5 tons to travel at a faster speed than their larger brethren, made them very attractive propositions. Many showmen turned to the smaller tractors, produced by manufacturers such as Tasker of Andover. Apart from their size, they were identical to the road locomotives, but had the advantage of being easier to handle. Frances Brown recorded how Joe Matthews (see Chapter 3) bought a series of Taskers, starting with a 3-ton compound of 1905 and ending with a 5-tonner of 1914. Known to the family as 'Little Giants', they were very highly thought of and very much a family concern. Joe's sons all proved adept at maintenance and repairs, Tom and his sister Annie turned out to have a fine artistic sense in applying the decoration and the whole family could take over the driving. Surprisingly perhaps, for those times, the daughters were included in those who could be entrusted with the engines out on the road.

Engine driving was generally a full-time occupation, whether on the road or at the fair and most were, like the Matthews girls, members of the owners' families. Where a showman had a small family or several engines to run, drivers would have to be hired. They might stay with one family for years, but they were never on an equal footing: one absolute rule was that the driver should on no account start chatting up any of the daughters. The driver was lumped in with the other 'gaffs', the army of unattached fairground workers. Where the family had their richly appointed living wagons, the drivers had to find what accommodation they could. The black-faced, grease-encrusted men were no more popular with landladies than their fellow drivers in more conventional forms of road haulage, generally less so as they had to face a general prejudice against all fairground workers. Unlike the heavy hauliers, however, they did not even have the rough comfort of a bunk in a living van to look forward to at the end of the day. Many finished up bedding down in a truck or under the engine, while bath night consisted of a bucket full of hot water drawn from the injector. If the engines were worked exceptionally hard, so too were the men who tended them. But theirs was a way of life that

LEFT: The Fowler and the gallopers are frequently to be seen in company. The engine here has its extension chimney in place to carry smoke above the crowds.

RIGHT: The showman's engine is always an attraction in the show ring. This is no accident: they were originally designed to attract attention and draw in the crowds.

had its compensations in their camaraderie, and freedom from petty restrictions typified life at the fair.

World War I marked a period of great change for the showmen, as indeed it did for everyone. Before the war, many had still persevered with horses, but with the scarcity and high cost of fodder during those years, most had been forced to let them go. In 1918, there was suddenly a vast array of cheap ex-army motor vehicles available together with portable generators. They may never have had the glamour of steam, but they did the job and were soon a familiar sight, though they always looked sadly drab alongside their sparkling rivals. Fowlers even made a brief foray into the enemy camp in 1935, the year after the last steam engine left the works. They built a diesel truck, specially designed with a dynamo permanently mounted behind the cab and with big spoked wheels, notably like those of the traction engine. In their advertising they listed the advantages of motor power over steam power:

No driver required when generating on the fairground
No getting up steam
No picking up water on the road
No clinkering up
No plugs to drop or loss of steam at a crucial time
No washing out
No leaking tubes
No floods of water around the engine on the fairground

All very true, no doubt, but to many it smacked of treachery. It was not, in any case, a success and the first Fowler diesel for showmen turned out also to be the last.

The showmen stayed with their steam engines for a long time, not out of sentiment for a commodity they could not afford, but because for many years they did a better job than their motorised rivals. Similarly, in America, where one would expect an eager rush for the new, the motor vehicle did not find an early home. American shows and circuses were not even enthusiastic users of steam haulage on the roads. With the long distances between sites, they relied very heavily on the railways and elsewhere they remained true to the horse. A remarkable photograph taken as late as 1931 in New York shows the biggest tented show of them all, Ringling Brothers and Barnum and Bailey, with everything being moved by horses, generally harnessed six to a team. In Britain, showmen recognised traction

engines as being powerful enough for the biggest loads and just as importantly they were incredibly tough and reliable. All kinds of things might go wrong, steam might be leaking out all over the place, but somehow there always seemed to be a way to keep the engine running and the ride moving. And in the last years of steam at the fair, improvements were being made that helped to keep the engines competitive.

One notable change came with the introduction of the solid rubber tyre, which in Britain became virtually universal after the passing of a ponderously named piece of legislation: The Road

Vehicles (Showman's Tractors & Heavy Locomotives) Regulations 1927. This reduced the road tax on showmen's engines, on the grounds that they spent more time standing in fields than they did out on the road, but with the proviso that to earn the reduction they had to be shod in rubber. This and other changes in the law affecting speed limits made fast runs a real possibility for the very first time. The new generation of engines by Fowler and Burrell were among the most impressive ever built. On one recorded run a Fowler Big Lion hauled a huge dodgem ride, mounted on three trucks, at speeds that reached

up to 18mph (29 km/h). This was the heyday of steam, but it was destined to be short-lived.

The world of the 1920s and 1930s was very different from that of the pre-war years. The heavily gilded and elaborately decorated rides seemed like anachronisms, reminders of a world that had gone forever, as out-of-date as the Victorian parlour with its heavy mahogany furniture with bulbous legs, and dark plush and lace curtains. The new age was lighter, brighter and faster. One of the attractions that epitomised this was the Dodgems, or bumper cars, which were patented in 1921. In the earliest version they

ABOVE: This set of gallopers seen at Cromford steam fair, England, has traditional decoration and a central organ, while the lights are beginning to glow in the dusk.

RIGHT: The Lincoln manufacturers, Clayton and Shuttleworth, do not rank among the best-known builders of fairground engines, but here is a splendid example of their work.

were miniature cars with electric, or even petrol, engines, which could be driven round in an enclosed arena. These usually carried official notices explaining that the idea was that drivers should demonstrate their skills by dodging the other cars. No one of course paid any attention to that – they simply got on with the much more entertaining activity of ramming another vehicle, preferably one driven by young and attractive representatives of the opposite sex. The popular version that finally evolved took their power through conductor poles, rather as trams did, connecting to an overhead mesh. Rides looked to the future not the past. Out went the stately steam gallopers and in came such streamlined newcomers as the Moon Rocket, a ride in which rocket-shaped cars sped round a circular track, built in Germany in the 1930s and soon popular throughout Europe. Furthermore, no one wanted a fairground organ playing Strauss, when you could have the latest song of the day performed by a popular singer on the Panatrope, using gramophone and loudspeaker. The fact that, in spite of their age and the huge and growing demands being made on them, the showmen's engines still held their place for so long is a tribute to their unique qualities. It was becoming clear by the 1930s, however, that their days were numbered. How long it might have continued can only be a matter of conjecture, but the signs were not propitious. Savages, who had built so many successful rides and the engines to haul them, were steadily losing ground to a new generation of builders providing all-electric rides. The old engine factories were closing their doors or converting to motor manufacture. Whatever future there might have been was abruptly stopped when the world was again engulfed in war in 1939. The age of the steam fair had, it seemed, ended for ever.

CHAPTER 5

THE STEAM ROLLER

The steam roller managed to make an appearance at the very beginning of this book, but not a lot has been heard of it since. The reason for its absence is a simple one: for a very long time no such machine was needed. Why that should have been the case is a more complex matter to deal with. It brings us back to the roads themselves, the state of which was absolutely crucial to the whole development of the traction engine. It is difficult for us to appreciate, or even believe, just how bad many main roads were even in the late eighteenth century. In America roads were just as bad and, if one is to

ABOVE: Thomas Aveling designed his first steam roller in 1865, and Aveling and Porter (later Aveling and Barford) dominated the British scene. This is a typical product.

Let me most seriously caution all travellers, who may accidentally purpose to travel this terrible country, to avoid it as they would the devil; for a thousand to one but they break their necks or their limbs by overthrows or breaking downs. They will here meet with ruts which I actually measured four feet deep, and floating with mud only from a wet summer; what therefore must it be after a winter?
(Six Months Tour Through the North of England, Arthur Young, 1769)

believe Western films, they stayed that way for a century after Young was making his travels in Britain. The image we all have is of the stagecoach racing down a dusty dirt road, pursued by Indians, outlaws or whatever dangers the writer and director have contrived. Arthur Young, on one of his many agricultural tours of Britain (see Chapter 1) had the following to say about a road in Lancashire. Remember, he is not speaking of some remote country lane, but the brand new turnpike, supposedly constructed to the very highest standard:

Improvements were on the way however, and the modern road system could fairly be said to have its origins in France in the 1770s. Pierre Trésaguet's system began with digging a trench, the bottom of which had a definite camber. On this a foundation layer of large stones was laid, and then the surface was built up using stones of ever decreasing size. This method of building was improved upon by Thomas Telford, working in Britain. His trench had a flat bed, which was then built up with carefully positioned stones to create the cambered surface. All the stones

LEFT: The might and power of the steam roller, which was to revolutionise road-building technology, is evident here in this magnificent Aveling and Porter engine, which dates back to around 1912.

ABOVE: The massive roller that set Aveling and Porter on its way being put to work at Hyde Park in London in 1866. Similar engines were soon to be seen in America in the parks of New York.

were precisely graded and the whole was topped by gravel. A vital part of the Telford system was good drainage.

Telford roads were excellent but very expensive to construct. A cheaper alternative was suggested by his contemporary and fellow Scotsman, John Loudon McAdam (1756–1836). He recognised that compacted soil was itself a perfectly adequate foundation, provided it could be kept absolutely dry. So, where others had dug a trench and laid courses of stone below the surface of the ground, he flattened the ground and built up his roadway, once again using compacted, graded stones. His method was widely adopted and his descriptions of road making were translated into many languages. In 1827, he was appointed surveyor-general of British roads and engineers came from all over Europe and America to see his works.

Good roads became established in many countries, though nowhere with such enthusiasm as in Britain. Here there was an average of 5 miles (8km) of road for every thousand hectares of land, compared, for example, with just 1.5 miles (2.5km) in the technologically advanced country of Prussia. The system was also brought into use in America in the early nineteenth century, with

the first turnpike road being built in Virginia. This was the road from Little River to Alexandria, which was opened as a toll road in 1805, and remained in much the same state, with no attempts at improvement, for the next hundred years. The truth was that no one could see much point in improving the old style roads once the modern rail road had arrived, and indeed the roads were perfectly adequate for the loads they were expected to carry. By the 1830s, mail coaches in England were averaging as much as 10mph (16km/h) on the main roads, and the only complaints that were heard seemed to be from those who thought they were too good. Such speeds were considered dangerous and reckless and things were much better when there was a good layer of mud to slow everything down.

In Europe things were slightly worse – or better if you were one of the conservative faction. The French *wagon postal* ran at a more modest 6mph (10km/h) on the somewhat poorer roads. But things were getting better everywhere, and Austria was among the first countries to set up a central road authority in the early nineteenth century.

The roads of the nineteenth century were certainly a great

improvement on those of the eighteenth century, but once they were laid down little more needed to be done: the weight of everyday traffic was considered all that was necessary to compact the surface. It was a job that was almost certainly better carried out by a roller, but it was not thought to be essential. But by now alternative materials were being considered that required a very different treatment.

Concrete roads were briefly fashionable, and became quite common in Austria from around 1850, but failed to find more general acceptance. Far more important was the use of asphalt. In 1712, a Greek doctor, Eyrinis d'Eyrinis found a natural source of rock asphalt in Switzerland. He discovered that by blending the powdered rock with hot pitch he could make what we would call asphalt mastic which could be used to create durable flooring. There were to be many attempts to use the new material for road building, starting in Paris with experiments on two of the Seine bridges and the Place de la Concorde in 1835. By the late nineteenth century, three different types of asphalt road surface had been developed, but a feature common to all was that it was essential to compact them with a heavy roller. The other not dissimilar material that became available for road construction was heavy tar, a by-product of the rapidly developing chemical industry of the late nineteenth century. When this was applied as a top dressing to roads built with the McAdam system, the result was known as tarmacadam, or more simply tarmac. Once again, the roller was needed to produce a satisfactory watertight, even surface. The technology was in place to produce decent roads. All that was needed was the political will to authorise spending the money, and this was only to come when other changes in the world of transport made it inevitable.

Of all the vehicles that one might think of as candidates for forcing through a change of heart with regard to road building, the humble bicycle would probably not feature very high on the list. When the first bicycles appeared in Britain they were predictably sneered at by the horse-riding gentry, and cyclists were scornfully referred to as 'cads on casters'. But prejudice had to bow down to fashion, when it was the young and wealthy who took to wheels. Legislators who could happily ignore the pleas of haulage contractors had much more difficulty withstanding the demands of their own sons and daughters.

It was the development of the motor car, however, that made the decisive difference. The older forms of transport with their wide, heavy wheels did their bit in flattening and hardening road surfaces. The motor vehicle on the other hand, with its

BELOW: An advertisement from the 1920 catalogue shows the 'scarifier'; the spiked attachment that can be seen was used to break up the surface of the old road before the new one could be laid.

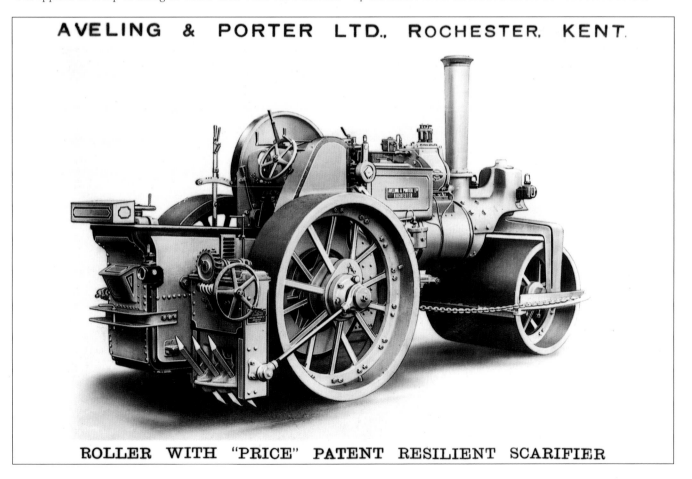

AVELING & PORTER LTD., ROCHESTER, KENT.

ROLLER WITH "PRICE" PATENT RESILIENT SCARIFIER

pneumatic tyres, had quite the opposite effect. They 'sucked' at the road surface, pulling at the grit and the result was that every passing motor car came complete with its very own personal cloud of dust. Water carts could be used to lay the dust, at least temporarily, but what was really needed was a system that would stop it forming in the first place. In 1902 a gentleman called Guglielminetti coated an old macadam road near Monte Carlo with a surface of tar, and the shape of roads to come was made clear. It was equally clear that a heavy roller was essential,

and as the material to be rolled was hot tar, it was equally obvious that the roller would need to be mechanised.

The road roller initially appeared at a time when road improvements first got under way. Jacob Leupold of Leipzig, Germany, was the author of a treatise on the latest inventions, the *Theatrum Mechinerum*, published in 1725, which showed an iron roller, weighing around a ton, designed to be drawn by horses. However, the rollers were not an immediate success as most roads were so bad that the heavy roller simply did more

EARLY INNOVATIONS

The first steam rollers were designed in France. The version built by Lemoine in 1859 was not a success, but the second by Ballaison of 1862 was a great improvement. The prototype weighed 17.5 tons and was powered by a 5-hp engine. It was manufactured by Gellerat et Cie of Paris from 1864, who supplied two versions, an 8.5-ton and a 15-ton roller. Development was also going forward in Britain, though the early experiments were not very fruitful. William Bray built what he called a steam roller, but it was really no more than a common road roller pulled by a traction engine instead of horses, but it was given a trial in the streets of London in 1859.

A less likely centre of innovation was Calcutta, where the Birmingham engineer W.E. Batho and the chief engineer of Calcutta W. Clark patented a design in 1863. Batho was destined to have a major role in the development of the roller, for he was soon to join the man who did more than anyone to produce the roller we know today, Thomas Aveling of Rochester in Kent. His early work with traction engines has already been mentioned (see Chapter 2), and it is not altogether certain when he began to take an interest in road rollers. A popular story has it that he was watching the reconstruction of The Esplanade at Rochester in 1857 and was struck by the effort required by the men who were painfully hauling a crude roller, made up of a heavy iron cylinder packed with cement, to level the stones. Always a man with an eye for an absurdity, and such work clearly was an absurdity in the steam age, he entered the fray in 1865. Like Bray he used a towed roller, an unlikely device made out of a 10-ft (3-m) diameter cast-iron bridge pier section. He very soon realised, however, that the wheels of his traction engine were actually a good deal more effective at levelling the ground than the ungainly roller it was dragging along and manoeuvring with extreme difficulty. The next step was obvious: to convert one of his standard 12 nominal horse power traction engines. This was done by enlarging the rear driving wheels, adding 6in (15cm) to the diameter and doubling the width to 3ft (1m). This produced an impressive force on the ground of 3 tons per square foot (0.28 tons per square metre).

At the same time he decided that something had to be done about the problem of steering. This was the time when a lot of thought was being put into the question of the best way to steer traction engines, and Aveling's own solution had been to have an extra pilot wheel poking out in front of the engine. This system had not worked well with the towed roller, which had proved difficult to manage and required considerable effort from the

damage to an already fractured surface. But a century later, when road construction had improved, they were in use in France, Hanover and Britain. Even so, they were not very popular as they suffered from one great disadvantage – before the roller could be brought to bear on the carefully prepared surface, horses had to trample all over it. It was generally thought that the roller did little more than repair the damage done by the beasts that were pulling it. Only a mechanical roller would really bring the solution.

steerer. An added disadvantage was that the pilot wheel tended to cut a deep groove through the rolled surface. So for his first genuine steam roller, he came up with a system of steering wheel and chain linkage which was not only a solution to the roller problem but was to be adapted for general use for all traction engines. The first engine was tried out on a contract for Her Majesty's First Commissioner of Works in Hyde Park, London, on the night of 1 December 1866. A contemporary illustration shows it steaming through the park, its way lit by a man walking in front and carrying two large lanterns. A whole new enterprise was under way.

Thomas Aveling, then of Aveling and Porter and later Aveling and Barford, was destined to dominate the whole world of steam rollers. Each one they produced had a symbol on the front of a rampant horse, taken from the banners of the Saxon brothers, Hengist and Horsa, who invaded England and established the Kingdom of Kent in around 450AD. Below the horse was a scroll with the single word *Invicta*, meaning 'unconquered', and

certainly no one ever managed to remove Aveling from their pre-eminent position in the world of steam rollers. The rampant horse was destined to travel the world. The local pride of Aveling, a Kentish man, probably dictated the choice of emblem, but in any case it was particularly appropriate. The loose stone chippings that provided the surface for so many roads when the steam roller first appeared may have been perfectly satisfactory underneath carriage and wagon wheels, but they could be very hard on horses' hooves, and if not properly laid and firmed down could inflict very painful injuries. The smooth, steam-rolled surface was a very real blessing, and if horses can be said to look happy, then there does seem to be the hint of a contented smile on the face of the Aveling horse.

The steam roller came at just the right time. In Britain, new bodies had been set up by the Municipal Corporation Act of 1835, and in the process the work of highway maintenance was passed to new administrative bodies, charged with making improvements. It was not a rapid process – few things in local government ever are – but there was real enthusiasm in those towns and cities that had grown to prosperity with the industrial age. And such towns were not just getting richer, they were getting bigger as well. For example, Manchester, in northern

BELOW: The rampant horse, which was to become the emblem of the firm of Aveling and Porter, was derived from the banner of the ancient kingdom of Kent, England, where the company was based.

AVELING & PORTER ROAD ROLLERS
e....Supplied to Sydney City Council...e

SYDNEY
CITY BRIDGES 1ST
No I

...Supplied 1924...

44 years old.
— STILL IN SERVICE —

ABOVE: Aveling and Porter were always keen to advertise the durability of their products and their long manufacturing tradition, and this was to extend well into the diesel age.

England, had a population of around 40,000 in 1770 and had expanded to ten times that number a century later. These new centres had a great sense of civic pride. This was expressed in the splendour of a new Gothic Town Hall or, in a more practical way, with new and better streets. And they were not afraid of new technology – it was, after all, new technology that had created their wealth. So when it came to repaving their streets it was only natural that they should turn to the man who was pioneering new developments, Thomas Aveling.

In March 1867, one of the principal technology journals of the day, *Engineering*, announced that Aveling had an order for a 22-ton roller for Liverpool:

It is to be the same as that now working in Hyde Park viz,
a 12-horse traction engine with its driving wheels weighted,
each to be between five and six tons.
Nearly twenty applications have been made to
the same makers from other corporations relative to the
supply of similar engines.

The new orders came from important boroughs, including Sheffield, Leeds, Darlington, the London Borough of Islington and, nearer to home, Maidstone in Kent. But whatever the journal might have said, the Liverpool engine was not the same as its predecessor. The two steering wheels had been brought close together to create what was, in effect, a single roller. This was a great improvement. What was definitely not an improvement was the decision to reverse the usual arrangement by applying the drive to the front wheels and steering with the rear, which seems to defy all logic. It was not an arrangement that Aveling persisted with for long, and soon using the front roller for steering, with drive to the rear wheels, became accepted as standard. It was, in any case, a huge success, and not just in Britain. The engines were exported all over Europe, to America and the Far East. The very first steam rollers to be used in the United States were Avelings which were set to work in Brooklyn and Central Park, New York, in 1869. The Brooklyn engine worked for two months night and day in Prospect Park, and at the end of the trial the Chief Engineer wrote this glowing testimonial: 'One day's rolling at a cost of ten dollars, gives the same result as two days rolling with the old seven ton roller, pulled by eight horses at a total cost of forty dollars' (*A Hundred Years of Road Rollers*, Aveling &

Barford, 1965). This encouraged American engineers to tackle the problem for themselves, and in 1873 Andrew Lindelof of New York took out the first American patent for a steam roller.

Aveling continued to make changes in design, and as with the steering, some of the changes he made were to become regular features of all traction engine design. One of the problems was caused by the practice of bolting the moving parts directly to the boiler, which while economical in terms of materials, set up strains which could lead to the creation of holes and loss of steam. He hit on the good idea of extending the sides of the firebox upwards to create what became known as the 'horn plates'. These were rigid, independent of the boiler and proved very sturdy. They were soon incorporated into all engines. Some new ideas, however, were less successful. After he had reverted to conventional rear wheel drive and front wheel steering, he divided the front roller into two conical sections, which were believed to work better on a cambered road. In fact, they proved liable to skidding. Variations could always be made to meet customers' own special requirements, so that, for example, in 1912 Aveling was supplying engines for France with particularly large rollers. These proved to be very effective, and were used on rollers for the home market a few years later.

The export business was always important to Aveling, and in 1873 they took a steam roller to the Universal Exhibition in Vienna. It was a huge success, being awarded the Order of Franz Joseph as the outstanding exhibit of the whole show. That did no harm at all to the international order book and the conical roller Avelings went around the world, one of them arriving to start work with the Oslo Municipal Road Department in 1878. The design may have had its critics, but this old engine puffed its way around the streets of Norway's capital right through to 1960. The retirement party was a grand occasion. Gleaming and shining, freshly polished and burnished, the fine old engine made the final journey past a guard of honour of road workers. It trundled along behind a brass band until it reached the retirement home, the Technical Museum in Oslo where it remains a prize exhibit, almost certainly the oldest surviving steam roller in the world.

The conical roller's career was brought to an end with the introduction of the asphalt surface. The skidding tendency was not particularly important on stones, and indeed was generally thought to be quite a good thing, applying extra pressure. But on asphalt, the sideways movement of the two shaped rollers tended to carry the material with it, producing a ridged surface. So out they went, and in came the familiar cylindrical rollers. There was still a small variation in size on the driving wheels, with the diameter of the inner rim being something under 1in (2cm) less than the outer, an arrangement that was intended to

ABOVE: As with modern road building and repairs, much of the work was done by contractors who, like this British firm based in Hampshire, would have invested in their own steam roller.

reduce wear by fitting the wheel more closely to the curve of the camber. It became a standard arrangement from 1878. Aveling received their full share of honours, with gold medals at international exhibitions from Paris to Philadelphia. The final change brought in by Thomas Aveling himself was the introduction of the compound engine, which went into full production in 1886. In the first version, the two cylinders were set one behind the other in tandem formation, but that was very short lived, and later models all had the familiar side-by-side arrangement.

AVELING'S LEGACY

Thomas Aveling was without doubt the most important individual figure in the development of the steam roller, and even in his own lifetime the company he had founded was beginning to change its character from being just one among many traction engine builders to a roller specialist. In fact, during the eighty years that passed between the first steam roller being produced

and the last, two thirds of the Rochester production was devoted to rollers. That makes the very impressive figure of over 8,000 machines, carrying the rampant horse all around the world. The records show that half the engines went for export, but there were still enough left over in Britain to give Avelings a clear majority on the home front.

After the founder's death, the company continued in Rochester as Aveling and Porter. One reason for their success was their adaptability in changing circumstances. The introduction of hot tar made it important that a roller should be able to reverse very quickly, in order to continue working the material while it was still hot and to avoid it sinking down into the soft tar if forced to stand still. Earlier models had had to close the steam valve down before reversing. The 1902 roller was the first to try and overcome this problem: it was a tandem, a two-wheel roller that could roll the same strip in either direction. The use of tandems was not a new idea: the French Gellerat and the

ABOVE: An intruder into the ranks of the Avelings. This is a rare survivor from the few rollers built by Burrell. Like all the engines they produced, it is an impressive and handsome machine.

American Lindelof engines had both been tandems, but the Avelings were the first to be designed specially for work on asphalt. They did not represent a final solution to the problem of quick reversing. That arrived with the 'coffee pots', so called from their centrally placed vertical boilers. This provided steam to a duplex engine, one with two cylinders, but unlike the compounds, of equal size and working independently. There was no flywheel and an eccentric valve gear, known as a Klug gear, made instant reverse a reality.

During the war years of 1914–18, Aveling and Porter, like other manufacturers, were entirely occupied with supplying the military demand for machines of all kinds, and had no time to think very much about possible new developments for rollers. As

peace came, they realised that the Rochester works were now running behind the times, not a position Aveling and Porter favoured. The problem was not so much in the engines themselves, but in production methods that still relied on the old techniques of assemblage. The world, however, was moving rapidly towards mass production and the use of interchangeable parts. They reorganised the whole factory and produced a new range of designs. Customers could choose from a list of rollers from 6 to 20 tons and had a choice of single or compound engines. The one fundamental change was to move from slide gears to piston gears. The company claimed they offered greater efficiency, but it was also true that they were easier and cheaper to make. Customers were not always convinced of their value.

One familiar problem that was likely to be met out on the road came when an engine with a full boiler had to negotiate a steep hill, when water could tip into the cylinders. With the old slide valves it would have found its way out again, but with a piston valve it was trapped and the only escape was by blowing the covers. Spring-loaded release valves were introduced, but the problem was never completely overcome.

ROLLER MANUFACTURERS

Avelings were by no means the only roller manufacturers. A contemporary of Thomas Aveling was William Barford, head of the Queen Street Engineering Works at Peterborough, makers of agricultural equipment. In 1872 Thomas Perkins joined the firm which soon became Barford and Perkins, and they decided to concentrate on rollers, not road rollers so much as heavy rollers for parks and sports grounds. They made one brief excursion into steam rollers, with what they called a 'semi-tandem', an odd name since all the compacting was actually done through

BELOW: This huge Aveling and Porter compound with its immense side tanks, each holding approximately 500 litres (110 gallons) of water, was sent from Britain to Toulouse, France, in 1912.

the single driven roller. The most striking feature was the vertical boiler, rearing up in the middle of the machine. It was a short-lived venture and the company's rollers soon reverted to old designs, intended only to be worked by men or horses. This state of affairs continued until the arrival of the internal combustion engine. Their first diesel roller was built in 1904, and by 1921 they had become involved with Aveling and Porter and other manufacturers in setting up an industry-wide sales organisation, Agricultural Engineering Ltd. The large group soon broke up, but Barford and Aveling found that their two companies complemented each other very well, and they amalgamated. It was a sensible step, for it meant that both steam and diesel rollers were available from the same company, but as time went on there was an unstoppable movement towards the latter. The process was complete by 1947, when the very last steam roller left the Rochester works. It was not quite the end of steam, however, for as late as 1950 a special order for Aveling rollers was carried out under contract by Armstrong Vickers. The last of the rampant horses were sent across the oceans to Thailand and Indonesia.

Avelings, in various partnerships, may have dominated the steam roller world in a way that no manufacturer ever managed

to dominate the wider field of traction engine manufacture as a whole. They did not, however, have a monopoly. Robey, for example, became particularly well known for their tandems. The ultimate development of the tandem system came through the work of R.E.B. Crompton (see Chapter 3). He suggested having not two rollers in line, but three. The idea was tried by Barford and Perkins with an oil engine in 1912, but the most spectacular version must be the Robey tri-tandem. They were most extraordinary looking vehicles with a comparatively small front roller and two massive rear rollers, linked by chain drive. Even the boiler was unconventional. It was Robey's own design of stayless boiler with a round firebox. The reversing was through a Stephenson link, the kind that had been tried and tested on the railways for many years. Robeys had a reputation for being particularly good for asphalt, and one of their biggest customers was the Limmer and Trinidad Asphalt Company, which took its name from its sources of asphalt – Limmer in Hanover, Germany, and the famous Asphalt Lake in Trinidad.

Individual companies had their own answers to different design problems. Steering on most engines was low geared and made easier by having the front roller split, each half being able to rotate individually. Wallis & Steevens, however, used differential gears, but as most steam rollers scarcely moved at more than 2mph (3km/h) and then mostly in straight lines it seems a touch over-sophisticated. Burrells adapted their single-crank compounds to steam rolling in 1891, and they proved a very successful export line, a large number going to Saxony in Germany. The Germans themselves went into production with some very powerful machines such as the single roller Berliner Maschinenbau. Perhaps the most sophisticated of all engines was the Universal built by Marshalls of Gainsborough, first seen in 1926. It had duplex cylinders and a quick reversing radial valve gear. The weight of the rollers could be adjusted by water balancing and the rear wheel could be altered for different cambers. Like the Wallis & Steevens, it had differential gears.

All kinds of refinements were added over the years. Boiler feed pumps working from the crankshaft soon became common. Rollers were originally solid metal, and once they had worn they could only be replaced by entire new rollers. After 1910, they were provided with renewable plates, greatly reducing the maintenance bills for the owners. Convertibles were built in which the rollers could be replaced by wheels, turning the roller into a road locomotive. Various bits and pieces were added including a spray for damping down the road and a scarifier for attacking the surface of the old road. This raises the question of

RIGHT: This Aveling and Porter, built in 1928, was specially fitted with an oil-fired boiler to meet the needs of a particular customer, a Mr W.H. Cullington of Buenos Aires.

just what was involved in building new roads and the part played by the steam roller.

The simplest use was the earliest, doing no more than compacting the surface of a stone road. Life became more complicated with the arrival of road surfaces involving the application of hot tar. This really became important in Britain after the Road Board was set up in 1909. It imposed a new licence system on motors and a fuel tax to raise revenue specifically for road improvement. County councils and other local authorities set to work, either with their own men or using contractors to transform the country. Rather than building new roads, they concentrated on converting the old roads to a tarmac or asphalt surface. One of the noticeable features of photographs, especially of rural areas, of this period is that all the white and dusty roads now begin to turn black. Most of the work, however, was done by hand, with the steam roller as virtually the only mechanical aid.

Steam roller crews travelled as other engine crews did, with their living van and water cart in tow. Once on site, the first job was to prepare for laying a new surface by getting rid of the top of the old. That is where the scarifier came in. The most popular model was produced by Morrison, Allen and Price and consisted of a heavy, spiked roller which attached to the rear axle and could be used with the engine working forward or in reverse. It needed a little help to get started, but once in place, the position of the spikes was marked and hand picks were used to break into the surface. The spikes were then settled into the holes and as the roller moved slowly along, the surface was most satisfactorily ripped to pieces. The broken lumps were then shovelled out of the way by hand.

The mixture to be laid, the 'metal' as it was called, was generally prepared in special depots set up on site at the roadside. One might have thought that it would be simple enough to use some form of steam mixer, perhaps a small portable or an engine run off the roller's flywheel. Contractors showed little interest. Labour was cheap, so everything was done with hand tools, and mixing sand, gravel and hot tar with nothing more than a shovel was not just hard work, but filthy work as well. Once ready, the hot mixture was brought on horse-drawn flats and shovelled, raked and rammed down by the men. A few rollers in later days had tar-spraying attachments, but these were the exception. Braziers of burning coke surrounded the scene, keeping the surface warm so that it could be worked, and the men also had to keep reheating the ends of their rakes and shovels. It must have resembled the medieval depictions of the inferno, as if the whole land was on fire.

LEFT: The 8-ton Royalty No 4860, produced in 1901. It is perhaps advisable not to enquire too closely after what happened to the driver after he had parked the roller!

ABOVE: Among the biggest users of steam rollers were local authority road departments. Here the entire Gloucestershire fleet is lined up outside Gloucester Gaol, England.

RIGHT: In the 1930s, Aveling and Porter became Aveling and Barford, but as seen here the design of their machines changed little. They were, however, soon to move over to motor rollers.

In assessing the role of the steam roller, it is fair to say that without it the modern road system could never have been developed, and without decent roads to drive on, the age of the motor vehicle would have been seriously delayed. The steam roller may not have had the glamour of the showman's engine, nor even seem as exciting as a big road locomotive, but it was more important than the former and, in the long term, probably made a more valuable contribution to the world of transport than the latter. If it had not existed, the road surfaces could not have existed either, for no other practical alternative for levelling and compressing was available. So, in a very real sense the steam roller was the author of its own demise. The arrival of the motor vehicle created the demand for better roads and for a different type of road. Once that was available then there was an incentive to improve the vehicles. Yet even when the diesel engine had developed into a powerful force that had all but swept the steam wagon into oblivion, the steam roller kept on going

The great virtue of the steam roller was its essential simplicity. Of all the machines that brought steam to the highways, the roller probably went through the least changes. When the last steam locomotive, *Evening Star*, was built for British Railways in 1960, there were still steam rollers at work. But by then, many of them were very old indeed, some having already recorded over half a century of use. They were the last of the line. Aveling and Barford were still in business, but now only diesel rollers came out of the factory. The glorious, but brief, age of working steam on the roads was coming to an end. The traction engine, in all its different forms, had become an historical relic, as quaintly old fashioned as the stage coach. But the steam men went down fighting and a surprisingly large number of engines were saved. This story will form the final chapter of this book.

CHAPTER 6

THE END OF AN AGE

When one considers that the first steam engine appeared at the end of the seventeenth century, but the first passenger vehicle to be powered by steam only appeared on the road in 1801, development seems to have been remarkably slow: The development of the internal combustion engine was incredibly fast by comparison. The idea of an internal combustion engine was not new: Huygens, who had inspired Papin's steam experiments (see Chapter 1), had ignited gunpowder in a cylinder, but it could hardly be called a practical machine. Apart from being quite alarming, it had to be stopped between each stroke to recharge it with powder. It was not until 1859 that the Frenchman Étienne Lenoir designed a gas engine, using an explosive mixture of gas and air, fired by an electric spark. This was a practical machine but was, like the early steam engines, rooted to the spot, if only because it needed to be connected to a gas supply.

Real progress came with the introduction of the four-stroke cycle devised by the German engineer N.A. Otto: induction, compression, ignition, and exhaust. He used it for a horizontal gas engine in 1878. It was a huge success and within a few

ABOVE: The development of the internal combustion engine, in the form of diesel tractors such as this American John Deere, posed a major threat to the survival of steam power.

years, the company he formed had sold over 30,000 four-stroke engines all around the world. It was still, however, very far from being an engine that could be used for transport. The first essential step was to change the fuel.

If Britain had led the world in the development of steam power, then the story was very different when it came to this new breed of engines. Where Otto had led, another German engineer Rudolf Diesel followed. He realised that when air was compressed, it heated up, and if it was then mixed with a fuel oil in the form of light droplets the latter would ignite. He took out his first patent in 1902 and the engine that still bears his name was born. It began as a stationary engine, but was soon to be set on the move. Gottlieb Daimler of Württemberg introduced the carburettor that added vapourised petroleum to air to create the explosive mixture for a four-stroke engine. At much the same time another German, Karl Benz of Mannheim was devising his first motor vehicle, which, unlike the Daimler, used a high-speed engine. Development now moved ahead at a furious pace and the motor industry was born. The new lightweight motors seemed to offer little threat to the

LEFT: A sad ending: this old portable engine once served the stone quarries of Portland, England, but has ended its life rusting in a field surrounded by weeds and scrap.

steam men, but the first real challenge was to come down on the farm, where the steam engine had itself mounted the first challenge to the horse.

It was inevitable that the geographic emphasis of progress would shift. The steam engine had been the ideal machine for Britain, a country that had been described as an island of coal. America, on the other hand, had oil. Also, there was a certain complacency in Britain, whose manufacturers had enjoyed a near monopoly of inventions during the Industrial Revolution years. The machines of that age were built to last, and last they did, so there was no great urgency about hunting for replacements. No one in Britain seemed to notice that other countries were not just catching up, but were overtaking. Where, for example, German manufacturers had followed British practice in traction engine construction, it was now the task of the more enterprising engineers and entrepreneurs of Germany to take the lead in the early motor age. And in the areas traditionally ruled by the traction engine, America was moving to the front. In 1889, the Charter Gas Engine Company of Chicago, Illinois, produced a wholly new type of vehicle – a farm tractor with an internal combustion engine.

The first threat that the tractor posed was to the steam plough. The plough had after all developed over very many centuries as a device to be pulled along behind an animal. The steam engine had been unable to duplicate this method of working and the steam plough, ingenious though it was, was never going to be the last word on the subject. Even the greatest of steam manufacturers began to think of making a change. The Case Steam Company had produced a tractor in 1892, but they had difficulty with the ignition system and went back to steam. Perhaps they felt the threat would never materialise and Case steamers continued to thrive, reaching a peak in 1910 when they were turning out over 2,000 traction engines a year. It was not to last: ten years later output had slumped to around 150.

But if Case were unconvinced by the motor tractor, others were more persistent. The Huber Manufacturing Company of Marion, Ohio, bought the Van Duzen gasoline engine company in 1896 and by 1898 they had sold their first batch of 30 tractors. It was a small beginning and development was slow: a decade later there were still only around a hundred tractors in use. That, however, was about to change. Henry Ford is famous for the introduction of the assembly line for the mass production of the Model T, which first appeared in 1908–9, selling nearly 18,000 in its first year. Improvements in the factory brought down the price and increased the sales to ten times that

RIGHT: Steam engine manufacturers fought the motor tractor with new lightweight models of their own. This one, known as *The Joker*, was built by Garrett of England.

figure in just five years. What is less generally talked about is their other product, the Fordson tractor, which if it did not have the sensational sales of the Model T was to transform the agricultural scene. Initial success was given a boost by the introduction of power take off in 1918, a system that used a shaft from the motor to power various implements. It helped to make the motor tractor all conquering. In the 1920s production of Fordsons topped the 100,000 a year mark and by 1950 there was a staggering 3,400,000 tractors in America alone.

THE BEGINNING OF THE END

This was not the only threat to steam power on the farm. From around 1900, large numbers of American companies were producing cheap, portable petrol engines which could be used for all kinds of different tasks. Many also found their way across the Atlantic and effectively replaced steam for a wide range of jobs. The final nail in the steam coffin was driven in with the arrival of the combine harvester, at first hauled by horses, but later self-propelled. It was the ideal implement for the vast grain fields of North America, even if it was not considered equally suitable for the smaller fields of Europe. Wherever it came into use, it took over one of the most important applications of the traction engine: threshing.

The tractor represented the greatest threat not just to the continued expansion of the traction engine, but to its very existence. Some manufacturers gave up the struggle, but others tried to fight the opposition on their own ground. Even in America, where oil was a cheap and economical fuel, there was an attempt to persevere with the old ways. In 1922–3 the International Harvester Company of Chicago, Illinois, produced two experimental tractors, looking superficially like their motorised cousins, but neither was taken beyond the prototype stage. The Bryan Company of Peru, Indiana, tried a compromise, producing a vehicle with a high-pressure tubular boiler, but fired by kerosene. The most ambitious was the Baker steam tractor, produced at their works in Swanton, Ohio. It used the very latest steam technology, with very high-pressure steam at 300psi (20.5 bar), a compound engine and automatic stoking. The problems of water supply were eased by using an automobile type fan-cooled radiator to condense the exhaust steam for recirculation. It was very light by traction engine standards, at a little over half a ton, and very manoeuvrable. It was a valiant effort, but a failure none the less, and within a year the Baker Company had joined the opposition.

The same story was repeated elsewhere. British manufacturers also mounted challenges. When Denzil Lobley of Garretts first encountered a Fordson he noted the particulars of cost and performance which, as he wrote to his Engineering Director, 'give me furiously to think of the future, if any, of steam' (quot-

ed in *The Age of the Traction Engine*, R. Whitehead, 1970). They made an effort and, being a Suffolk firm, named their new steam tractor after the famous heavy horse, the Suffolk Punch. Again new technology was incorporated including superheated steam at 570°F (300°C) being supplied to a double-cranked compound engine. A ploughing test against a motor tractor showed it coming off second best and the Suffolk Punch slid away into oblivion. One company, however, did enjoy a certain success. Sentinel had a very high reputation as manufacturers of steam wagons, and these at least were still holding their own in road transport. They used their expertise to produce the Sentinel-Roadless tractor which was intended for the very roughest work, such as forestry or difficult terrains overseas. With its caterpillar tracks it was claimed that it could climb a 1:1 slope, while with its strong draw-bar it could plough 18 acres (7ha) a day. An even bigger and more powerful version, the Rhinoceros, was produced specifically for the African market. The big Sentinels could undoubtedly outperform the best motor tractors on the market, but even the smaller versions cost five times as much as a Fordson.

Even if manufacturers had been able to reduce costs to a competitive level, this was a battle that was never going to be won. The customers liked the new machines, and it is easy to see why. On a cold, wet morning there is a great deal to be said for a machine that does not demand that you get up an hour or two before the farm work is due to start to clean out the dirt created on the previous day, light a fire and feed it while the water boils and pressure slowly rises. Instant starting was one of the strongest selling points for the new tractors, though the promoters seldom mentioned the dire effects of damp and cold on early ignition systems. Once under way, the tractors were lighter and easier to handle than their steam counterparts, yet performed just as well if not better. The end of steam was inevitable. What was true on the land was true on the road, even if not everyone saw this clearly. One of the great chroniclers of the steam engine, William Fletcher, could still write these words as late as 1904:

Every steam engine which passes along the street justifies the confidence placed in it; and unless the objectionable features of the petrol carriage can be removed, it is bound to be driven from the road, to give place to its less objectionable rival, the steam-driven vehicle of the day.

(Steam Carriages, William Fletcher, 1904)

This must rank as one of the all-time bad prophecies. Steam power was doomed and it seemed that by the middle of the twentieth century the only proper place for the faithful traction engine was the scrap heap. Fortunately, not everyone agreed.

In 1937, eight men met at a house in Orpington, Kent. They shared a passion for the old engines, and at the end of the meeting the Road Locomotive Society was born and the work of preserving traction engines had begun. It was not confined to Britain. It seemed that wherever the old engines were in use, there were enthusiasts ready to spend considerable amounts of time and money to restore them to a condition they had perhaps

BELOW: Arthur Napper and Old Timer preparing for the Appleford Rally of 1957, an event with its origins in Old Timer's famous race against a rival engine, Lady Grove, in 1950.

scarcely enjoyed since first passing through the manufacturers' gates. Some were destined to end up in museums as static exhibits, but for many of the new owners, steam engines that did not steam were sad anachronisms. They restored them to full working order and ran them for their own pleasure.

It was only natural that enthusiasts should meet to compare notes and engines, and it was equally inevitable that all enthusiasts should believe that their own particular pride and joy was the finest of them all. Just such a meeting took place in 1950 between Arthur Napper, owner of the 1902 Marshall Old Timer and Miles Chetwynd-Stapylton whose engine was a 1918 Aveling, Lady Grove. Arguments over the merits of the two

ABOVE: A poignant image of the old and the new: a portable steam engine, produced by the German manufacturer Esterer, is being given a chauffered ride through town.

engines went backwards and forwards, claims were met with counter claims, and there was really only one way to settle the issue. Steam would be raised and the giants would compete over a course set out at Napper's Berkshire farm. News of the race spread and crowds gathered to cheer the engines on their way. Victory went to the home team and *Old Timer*, but for Napper it was a revelation. Only a few could afford to purchase and restore a traction engine, but there were a great many who shared the owners' love of the grand old machines and would warmly welcome the chance to relive the glories of steam. So the steam rally was born, and this was soon to become a truly international phenomenon.

This seems a straightforward enough story, but it does raise some interesting questions. Why is there such enthusiasm and affection for machines that were built for such unromantic tasks as threshing corn and flattening roads? And what sort of people devote so much energy to their restoration? It might be thought that the answer to the second question could provide a clue to the first. If it turned out that the engines were mainly owned by those who had once worked with them, then one could see a

BELOW: From modest beginnings, the steam fair has grown to a massive event attracting huge crowds. Here a fine array of showmen's engines is seen in a traditional setting.

certain logic in that. But this is certainly not the case. The traction engine enthusiast really can come from any walk of life. There are even examples of what has been whimsically called 'nominative determinism'. For example, a certain Mr Crane, known to the author, began building model crane engines as a boy and ended up buying the real thing as an adult!

A MODERN ATTRACTION

It is not an exclusively male preserve and when two enthusiasts meet and marry, the affair is bound to end up as a steam extravaganza, as the following story illustrates. In Britain, the Rev Teddy Boston acquired a 1907 Aveling and Porter steam roller in 1960 and called the great beast *Thistledown*. Then, in 1927, he acquired a Foster agricultural engine that became *Fiery Elias*. In 1973, he married the secretary of the Market Bosworth Steam Engine Rally, Audrey Lee. The wedding procession consisted of *Thistledown* and *Fiery Elias* hauling a former L.M.S. Railway dray on which bride and groom rode in splendour, having left the church under a bridal arch of firing shovels. Whatever it is that makes a steam enthusiast, it seems to assume a major role in that person's life. Teddy himself was fond of quoting the Rev W. Awdry, author of the *Thomas the Tank Engine* books (in which Teddy himself sometimes appears in the guise of 'The Fat Clergyman')

on why so many clergymen are so keen. 'The steam engine', he said, 'is like the Church of England – the best way of getting to a Good Place'.

None of this gets us very much closer to an understanding of the fascination exercised by the engines on so many. For some it is the recreation of a world they had once known. Yet many enthusiasts are not old enough to have seen the engines in their working days, so that must be only a partial explanation. Question enough owners, however, and one thing becomes clear. There is something special about the nature of steam power itself, and it makes little difference whether it was originally applied to working looms in a mill or hauling express trains. The appeal remains. There is something elemental about the steam engine. You light a fire and boil water – actions that are familiar to all of us. And we can all see that steam can move things, even if it is only a pan lid on the stove. There are scientific laws explaining just how steam expands, equations for measuring the force it exerts, but you have no need of them to understand the basic principles – and when you see a traction

BELOW: In Britain, the London to Brighton run – inaugurated to celebrate the repeal of the Red Flag Act – still attracts vintage and veteran vehicles: a Burrell towers over a 1904 Peugeot.

engine, they are there on open display. There is the fire burning brightly and a boiler being heated to raise steam. And you can see, feel and hear the steam as it hisses out of valves and cylinders. Even in motion, you can see the pistons going in and out, see the connections to the crank and watch the wheels turn. The finer details of valves and cranks may be a mystery to the uninitiated, but the basics could hardly be clearer. To produce these words you are reading I have used my fingers on a keyboard and the words have appeared on a screen. I could stare at the computer as long as I liked, I could even take it to pieces, but I would still not see anything that would explain just what is happening. True, I could read up about electronics and chip design, but I still cannot see it for myself. How different the steam traction engine is – a self-contained unit using the basic elements of fire and water.

It may sound a trifle fanciful to talk of the appeal of elemental forces, but it seems that it really is something that all who care for steam are acutely aware of. Even the motor car suffers in comparison with the traction engine, for the motor is tucked away out of view, and in any case the parts move too fast for the eye to follow. The movements of the traction engine are slow and graceful in their elegance. Smooth, intricate movements do no more than reflect efficient design, and efficient design means that the machine works well.

The traction engine can really be appreciated to the full when it is doing the job it was designed to do. Michael Oliver, organiser of the Great Dorset Steam Fair in Britain, explained how the idea for a fair first came to him:

I'd been to one or two steam engine events
and I always noticed that when they took off to go home,
there was more interest in the engines loading on
the transporters than there was when they
were actually performing in the ring.

He determined to run a steam fair where, as far as possible, the engines would be seen at work. That he was right can be judged by the Dorset steam fair's success. The original showground at Stourpaine covered 500 acres (202ha). This turned out to be too small, so it was moved to an even bigger site nearer Blandford Forum. Today it can reasonably claim to be the biggest show of its kind in the world, and one at which the agricultural engines can actually be seen at work: corn is threshed and baled, and

RIGHT: Today, traction engines appeal to people from all walks of life. Here the driver of Goliath can be seen. A regular visitor to steam fairs, he spends his working days as a surgeon!

fields are ploughed by steam. These are not just fairground demonstrations, but the real thing, and once the show is over the fields will be replanted to supply the raw material for next year's thresher. It gives the unique opportunity to compare the steam plough to both its predecessor, the heavy horses, and its successor, the tractor. The heavy engines can also be seen at work. Tree trunks are hauled onto the site, and are taken over to the portable saw bench to be cut down into fence posts. Once again this is real work with a purpose, for the posts themselves are eventually used by the National Trust. Only one task of heavy haulage has no real practical use – moving the giant load. But even if the load is destined to move no more than perhaps a mile down the road, before it is turned and brought back again, the work done is real enough. It may require four or five engines to move the load, the organisers usually contriving for a steep hill to feature on the route. It is a magnificent recreation of a world that has not existed in earnest for at least half a century. The steam rollers may feel a little left out – it is not easy to arrange to resurface a road – but they can at least parade in the ring in front of an admiring public.

For many it is the showmen's engines that are the stars of the show. It is possible to see the fair as it might have been at the beginning of the twentieth century, and it is if anything even grander. Where in the old days the big fairs might have had a handful of engines, the Dorset show can muster forty and more at a time. They are seen at their best at night time, generating power for lights and rides. The big wheel turns, the gallopers gallop and the steam yachts swing, all to the accompaniment of dozens of steam organs. Over it all hangs the haze of steam and smoke, and the smells of steam perfume the air. It is no wonder that visitors turn up each year at this show in their tens of thousands. This is the steam rally at its grandest, but even the smallest bring in their admiring crowds.

Part of the appeal, as Michael Oliver noted, comes from seeing the engines arrive and depart, particularly those that travel under their own steam. This is especially true of those rare events staged in towns, such as that at Camborne in southwest England, which each year devotes a day to celebrating the works of its most famous son, Richard Trevithick. Whistles ring out among the shops, and wheels clank as the engines make their way through the streets to gather for the grand parade down the main street. Small country rallies may only be able to muster a few engines, but what is lacking in numbers is made up for in good will. Traction engine owners are, on the whole, a friendly lot and more than happy to talk about their charges, and even

LEFT: The steam fair is now an international phenomenon, with enthusiasts right across the world. Here a splendid collection of North American engines can be seen on show in Milton, Ontario.

entrust the steering, if not the actual driving, to complete novices. A regular feature of many shows is a competition, usually some form of obstacle race, where the general public do their best to coax the monsters into doing their bidding and following the course laid out in the arena. In this way, the engines live, the public get to see them at close quarters and a lucky few even get to ride. It is no wonder that the popularity of the rallies does not diminish with the years. And all the time new generations are being introduced to the delights of steam. At one rally, I saw a lady polishing her steam roller, while next to it her son was polishing his with the help of her very small, but no less eager, grandson.

LOOKING TO THE FUTURE

The future of the preserved traction engine seems assured for a good while yet, even if no one can prophesy how tastes will change. Perhaps one day a virtual reality traction engine will seem more attractive than the real thing: it will certainly be a good deal cleaner, cheaper and require less hard work! But is there a future for steam, not just in rebuilding old engines, but using steam power in new, imaginative ways? This might seem a pointless exercise in nostalgia, but the idea is being actively considered by some powerful bodies. A mention was made earlier of the American high-performance Doble sports car. What is not so well known is the work of the engineer, Abner Doble, on other uses of steam on road and rail, and few are aware that his ideas are still being actively considered. His story makes a fascinating footnote to the traction engine account, a tale of what was, what might have been and what still might come to pass.

The Doble system used steam at high pressure and temperature, associated with a double- or triple-expansion high-speed engine, exhausting to a condenser. It was both efficient and compact, and he developed his ideas with two German companies – Henschel & Son, of Kassel, and Borsig, of Berlin – and the British steam wagon manufacturer, Sentinel. Henschel and Borsig concentrated on producing rail cars which were put into service on the Lübeck–Büchener Railway. These two cylinder compounds could work up to the very high pressure of 1,145psi (80 bar). Sentinel, not unsurprisingly, concentrated on road locomotives, again using compound engines at the even higher pressure of 1,500psi (105 bar). Unlike the rail cars, the steam lorries never got beyond the prototype stage, even though they worked very well. Sentinel by then had decided there was no future for steam. But Henschel went on to take up the challenge, and built both steam lorries and steam buses. They will not be seen at rallies, but

RIGHT: Not all engines enjoyed long, uneventful working lives. Accidents were rare, but when they did occur they were spectacular, as this unhappy scene shows.

they were probably the last and most sophisticated development of the traction engine. The line ended in 1939 and production never restarted after the war.

This is not quite the end of the story. Following the oil crisis of the 1970s, designers and engineers in the United States began to think in terms of steam power. A Senate Committee met in 1983 to consider various ways in which steam could be generated very efficiently in a fluidised bed, which had the great advantage of producing less pollution than the internal combustion engine. And one of the proposals went back to using Doble's ideas. This was, however, to be a Doble engine with a difference, not driving a locomotive directly, but acting as an electrical generator. It seemed to be a new technology, but was it really so very different in principle from the old showman's engine? And who knows, as we face ever mounting traffic jams caused by floods of individual cars, perhaps it might even be allied to Crompton's old notion of the road train (see Chapter 3). These are the sort of ideas being looked at by big American corporations, not bodies well known for their interest in nostalgia. All one can say with certainty is that if there is to be a rebirth of steam power, it will not come in the shape of gleaming machines with polished brasses, urged on their way by sweaty men with shovels.

The traction engine in its glory day was a splendid machine, strong and versatile, adaptable to anything from ploughing a field to lighting a fairground. It is ironical that its earliest development led directly to the birth of the railways, for that sturdy infant was to go on to refute its parentage. Historical 'ifs' are futile, but it is a fact that development was greatly restrained by conditions which had nothing to do with technological possibilities and everything to do with politics and vested interests. When restrictions were finally removed it was already too late for the traction engine. The world had moved on, the nineteenth century had given way to the twentieth and a new generation of engineers and designers wanted to work on the technology of a new age: the internal combustion engine. It would be wrong, however, to think of the traction engine story as being one full of regrets and might-have-beens. The engines did their work and did it well. The fact that so many have survived in full working order perhaps as much as a century after they were built is itself a tribute to their sterling qualities. It is doubtful if we shall ever see such machines that combine beautiful simplicity, elegant decoration and massive strength again. So hats off and three loud blasts on the whistle for the traction engines. Long may they survive.

LEFT: All set to go; this beautifully restored Sawyer and Massey is ready to fire up to bring the great days of the traction engine back to life with power and noise.

141

INDEX

PICTURE CREDITS

Front cover photograph: Anthony Burton. Back cover photograph: John Skidmore.
Arkwright Society/Nottingham County Council: 48–49, 132 (b). **Tom Brogden**: 14. **Anthony Burton**: 60, 61
(Clyde Shipping Company), 83, 106 (tl), 126. **Deutsches Museum**: 19, 21, 31, 50, 51 (t), 70, 71, 132 (t).
Farmers Weekly: 32–33, 34, 40. **Henry Ford Museum & Greenfield Village Research Center**: 41, 43 (both), 58–59, 74–75.
Melvyn Green: 28–29, 46–47, 54–55, 106–107, 118. **Philip Hosken/Cornwall IOS**: 12–13.
Impact Photos: 68–69 (Roger Scruton), 74 (t) (Roger Scruton), 90–91 (Martin Black), 94 (tl) (Derek Redfearn),
134–135 (Martin Black). **INTERFOTO**: 64–65. **Lincolnshire County Council Archives**: 24, 77, 78–79, 108, 109, 111,
112–113, 114, 115, 116, 119, 120–121, 122–123, 124 (t), 124–125. **Martin Pavey**: 2, 5, 18, 81 (b), 82.
POPPERFOTO: 8–9, 22–23, 35, 72–73, 78 (t), 131, 133, 138–139. **Mike Schram**: 26, 27, 42, 51 (b), 136–137, 140–141.
Science Museum: 7, 10, 11, 16, 17, 44 (tl), 46 (tl), 53, 63, 66–67, 110. **John Skidmore**: 6, 20, 44–45, 52, 56–57, 76–77,
80–81, 84 (t), 84–85, 86, 89, 92, 93, 94–95, 96–97, 98, 102–103, 128–129.
TRH: 36–37, 39, 88–89, 99, 100–101, 104–105, 117, 127.

ACKNOWLEDGEMENTS

The author and Amber Books Ltd wish to thank the following for their help:
Melissa Haddock of the Henry Ford Museum and Greenfield Village Research Center; Melvyn Green;
Alan Mitchell and Jim Smith of the Arkwright Society in Nottingham; Martin Pavey;
Margrit Prussat of The Deutsches Museum in Munich; Mike Schram; John Skidmore;
Adrian Wilkinson of The Lincolnshire County Council Archives.